COAL MEASURE PLANTS

Composite restorations of Carboniferous plants. *Lepidodendron* in right foreground; *Sigillaria*, left foreground; *Cordaites* (left) and Tree-fern (right) in background; *Calamites* in outer circle. From Chamberlin and Salisbury's *Geology*, vol. ii. Henry Holt & Co., New York.

[Frontispiece

COAL MEASURE PLANTS

By

R. CROOKALL, Ph.D.

OF THE GEOLOGICAL SURVEY
OF GREAT BRITAIN

WITH FRONTISPIECE AND 39 PLATES
FIGURING 240 SPECIES

LONDON
EDWARD ARNOLD & CO.
1929

Printed in Great Britain by
UNWIN BROTHERS LIMITED, LONDON AND WOKING

PREFACE

Owing to the labours of the late Dr. R. Kidston, the use of assemblages of fossil plants in subdividing the British Coal Measures has now received general recognition. For the correlation of one coalfield with another, plant remains constitute as a rule the best, sometimes the only, available criteria. Their value in correlating individual coal seams has been less explored, and in this direction much detailed work remains to be done. In certain instances, however, it has been shown that seams can be recognised by the percentages of the various groups of plants occurring in the associated rocks.

This little book has been prepared as a brief and, as far as possible, non-technical introduction to the palæobotany of the British Coal Measures from the point of view of the external morphology, in the belief that it will commend itself not only to students of botany, geology, and mining, but to amateur naturalists who, living on or near our coalfields, have close at hand a rich and interesting field for research. There is no lack of excellent works on palæobotany, written mainly from the structural and evolutionary points of view (e.g. M. C. Stopes's *Ancient Plants*, Blackie & Son, 1910; D. H. Scott's *Studies in Fossil Botany*, A. & C. Black, Ltd., 1920, 3rd ed., vols. i and ii; A. C. Seward's *Fossil Plants*, Cambridge Biological Series, vols. i–iv, 1898–1919; R. Zeiller's *Éléments de Paléobotanique*, Paris, 1900; and M. Hirmer's *Handbuch der Palæobotanik*, München and Berlin, 1927).

In the present work are given figures of and brief descriptive notes on 240 of the more common and characteristic British Coal Measure plants. A species which is common is not necessarily characteristic and *vice versa*, and it has been necessary to include a number of more or less rare forms. The main object of the work is to assist in the identification of species with a view to their practical use in geology and mining. It is, however, intended only as an introduction to this aspect of the subject, and those interested would do well to pass from it to the more comprehensive works, among which may be mentioned:—

(1) R. Kidston's "Fossil Plants of the Carboniferous Rocks of Great Britain," *Mem. Geol. Survey of Great Britain*, Palæontology, vol. ii, parts 1–6, 1923–1925. (This work was left unfinished by the author and is to be completed as early as possible.)

(2) R. Zeiller's "Flore Fossile Bassin houiller de Valenciennes," *Études Gîtes Minéraux de la France*, Paris, Atlas 1886, Text 1888. (Zeiller's work

is useful in investigating Middle and Lower Coal Measure floras, though a number of the identifications now require revision.)

(3) W. Gothan's "Die oberschlesische Steinkohlenflora," Teil i, *K. Preuss. geol. Landes.* (N.F.), Heft. lxxv, 1913, Berlin, is particularly valuable in studying Upper Coal Measure plants.

(4) R. Kidston and W. J. Jongmans, "A Monograph of the Calamites of Western Europe" (Flora of the Carboniferous of the Netherlands and Adjacent Regions, by W. J. Jongmans, vol. i, *Meded. Rijksops. Delfstof.*, No. 7), Atlas 1915, Text 1917, Gravenhage. This provides a detailed account, excellently illustrated, of both the Upper and the Lower Carboniferous Equisetales.

A number of the photographs here given represent small sections (only) of certain of Dr. Kidston's plates which have been published in "Fossil Plants of the Carboniferous Rocks of Great Britain" mentioned above. For permission to reproduce these I have to thank the Controller of H.M. Stationery Office. Mr. W. Hemingway, of Derby, has also kindly allowed me to use a number of his photographs of specimens. These are indicated in the Explanation of Plates by the initials "(R. K.)" and "(W. H.)" respectively. The frontispiece is reproduced by courtesy of Messrs. Henry Holt & Co., New York. Plate I is based in part on the diagram by Dr. M. C. Stopes (*Ancient Plants*, p. 177) with the permission of the author and of Messrs. Blackie & Son, Ltd., and in part on diagrams by Professor E. W. Berry, with the permission of Johns Hopkins University (the original nomenclature, which is slightly different from that here employed, is retained).

LONDON,   R. CROOKALL.

  1929.

CONTENTS

9

COAL MEASURE PLANTS

CHAPTER I

INTRODUCTORY

A. *TYPES OF FOSSILISATION*

PLANT remains are common in certain of the sedimentary rocks which form a large bulk of the earth's crust. They may be preserved in four chief ways:

(1) **Incrustations** are formed after the following manner: the branch of a tree, shed or torn off during a storm, may fall into a neighbouring stream. As it floats down towards the sea, lake, or lagoon, the softer tissues decay and some of the twigs, leaves, and seeds which it originally bore may become separated from the branch and continue their journey alone. Gradually the air imprisoned in the plant-cells is replaced by water, the parts become waterlogged and sink to the bottom, and are embedded in the mud and sand constantly being brought down by the stream. The entombing mud is eventually converted into clay or shale and the sand into sandstone.* Leaves, on account of their shape, usually lie flat on the bed of the estuary or lagoon, the tissues continuing to decay until they are represented only by a thin coaly layer. Such incrustations, showing the shape of the leaves and the course of the veins, are common fossils. They are termed IMPRESSIONS.

The stem, on the other hand, being much thicker than the leaves, and being composed partly of delicate tissues (e.g. the pith) and partly of resistant material (e.g. the bark and the wood) decays unequally. Probably the pith is the first tissue to disappear (or it may have been absent from the adult stem), and the space rapidly fills with sediment which assumes the markings of the inside of the woody cylinder. Fossils formed in this way are known as PITH-CASTS (see Plate XXIV, *a–d*).

Like the pith, the cortical tissues and the bast are generally soft and rapidly

---

* Both clays and shales are formed by the compression and partial drying of muds. Clays are plastic and structureless and break with a more or less shell-like fracture. Shales, on the other hand, readily split in a direction parallel to the original bedding. Sandstones are formed by the cementation (usually by silica, carbonate of lime, or iron oxide) of particles of sand which are sufficiently large to be seen by the naked eye.

disappear. The sediments enclosing the outside of the stem take on the inequalities of the surface of the resistant bark, in the course of time hardening into a MOULD (Plate XXI, *a*). Meanwhile the wood and bark themselves have been carbonised and crushed, until, from a diameter of several inches, they may be reduced in thickness to but a fraction of an inch on the inside of the mould, and the internal space they originally occupied fills with sediment which in turn assumes the markings of the mould. This may be distinguished as a STEM-CAST (Plate XXXV, *a*), and it will be observed that, while the markings on the stem-cast are similar to those on the original stem, those on the mould are reversed (elevations which occurred on the stem being shown on the mould as depressions, and *vice versa*). Some seeds are also composed of concentric layers of hard and soft tissues, and may thus give rise to moulds and casts in fossilisation (e.g. Plate XXXVI, *d, e*). Many flat and soft seeds are preserved as impressions (Plate XXXVI, *m*).*

(2) In **mummification** those plant tissues which are more resistant to decay are partially or entirely preserved and, after suitable treatment,† can be examined under the microscope. The waxy coatings (cuticles) of leaves and stems, of spore cases, and of some seeds are particularly amenable to this form of preservation, and fragments of mummified tissue may be found here and there on impressions. Mummification generally occurs when plants are fossilised in a very fine clay, which, by excluding the air, hinders decay. Fine-grained shales and clays, which are often almost soapy to the touch, should therefore be carefully examined for fossils showing this type of

---

* In incrustations, as described above, the plant remains are enclosed by mineral matter deposited *from suspension in* the water which carried it. They may also be encrusted by mineral matter deposited *from solution*, forming a travertine. This is seen at the present day in the so-called petrifying waters of Yorkshire, where carbonate of lime is deposited on the vegetation over which they flow, as in other forms of incrustation, preserving the *form* of the plant only, not the *tissues*. Minerals deposited from solution in hot volcanic springs may produce either the incrustation or the petrifaction of plant remains. The well-known petrified (silicified) forest of Tertiary plants in Yellowstone Park, and the Lower Carboniferous plants petrified in limestone at Pettycur, Fife, are examples of this. Another example of the preservation of plants by precipitation of minerals from solution is seen in the plant fragments (as impressions and casts) in clay iron-stone nodules. The latter are common in certain Coal Measure rocks and were once extensively worked as a source of iron. The iron, dissolved in the waters, was precipitated and formed iron carbonate which, mixing with the mud in suspension, aggregated round shells, leaves, cones, etc., to form the nodules. Similar clay nodules can be seen forming at the present day round rubbish in the mouths of rivers. As they formed rapidly and in fairly tranquil water, any included fossils are usually well preserved, showing the attachment of leaves and seeds, microsporangia, etc., and this source of fossil plants should not be neglected. The nodules are difficult to split, however, and the late Dr. L. Moysey overcame the difficulty by first freezing and then throwing them into hot water, when they readily split along the line of weakness due to the presence of the fossil. Burial in *air-borne* deposits may also result in fossilisation (e.g. the volcanic ashes of the Pettycur district contain isolated petrified stems).

† The methods of treating impressions and mummified plant remains have been greatly improved in recent years by Dr. John Walton (see *Annual Report and Trans. Manchester Micro. Soc.*, 1926, p. 51, and *Congrès de Stratigraphie Carbonifère Heerlen*, 1928, Liége, p. 749), and by Mr. E. Ashby (see Professor W. H. Lang's Note in *Annals of Botany*, vol. xl, 1926, p. 710).

preservation. It is from such rocks that the only undoubted examples of Carboniferous Bryophytes have been obtained.

Sandstones, besides having a relatively coarse texture, admit a considerable amount of air, so that the decay of any included plants has been fairly rapid and more or less complete; good impressions in sandstones are therefore rare, but moulds and casts of roots, stems, and seeds may be common. Shales provide excellent impressions, the fine texture of the matrix reproducing the minute external details of the plant. Coals* contain innumerable mummified plant fragments; the best-known examples of mummification are the insects, flowers, pollen-grains, etc., preserved in amber (the fossilised resin of Tertiary and Quaternary Conifers).

(3) In **petrifaction** the plant remains were buried in sand or submerged in water charged with minerals, and the *tissues* were gradually replaced by, or included in, the minerals (chiefly lime or silica) deposited from solution. In this way an exact replica in stone of the original tissues was often formed. Petrifications have generally lost some of the outer layers, so that the external appearance of the plant remains unknown. In some instances the outer surface of a petrifaction shows the markings of the bark or other external features (i.e. the fossil may be regarded as both a petrifaction and an incrustation), and these are most valuable to botanists. Incrustations provide data as to the form of the plant, petrifactions as to its internal structure (and therefore as to the climatic conditions under which the plant lived and its relationships to other plants). The best-known petrifactions are the "coal balls" (more properly calcareous nodules)† originally found in the Upper Foot Coal of Lancashire and the Halifax Hard Bed of Yorkshire, but which have been

---

* Coal is a rock largely composed of mummified plant remains which are more or less impregnated by a fossilised jelly derived from their partial decomposition. Dry coals contain up to 10 or 15 per cent. of mineral matter. As the percentage of mineral increases in the rock, coals pass first into oil-shales, then into carbonaceous shales, and finally into ordinary shales.

† "Coal balls" occur as roughly spherical stones (either singly or in masses) embedded in the coal itself, and are therefore distinguished as *seam* nodules. They vary in size from that of a pea to two or three feet in diameter, but most frequently being of about the size of a potato. When found they are covered with a coaly layer and are therefore black, but on washing with dilute hydrochloric acid become grey. They consist of varying proportions of the carbonates of lime and magnesia, with certain impurities. Sections of these nodules show them to be composed of a medley of plant fragments which are penetrated in all directions by the rootlets of *Stigmaria*, etc., indicating that the débris accumulated *in situ*, in a swamp. The remains generally show the structure of swamp plants.

Roof nodules occur in the shaly roof of the same seams and generally contain fossil animals only: often, however, they also contain a single plant fragment, usually a stem or petiole or other resistant plant part (not delicate tissues such as the leaves, seeds, and rootlets which commonly occur in seam nodules), and this generally shows the structure of a land plant. Roof nodules contain marine shells (*goniatites*) which are absent from seam nodules. The isolation of the plant fragments, and the fact that they are accompanied by marine shells, show them to be remains which *drifted* out to sea above the sunken seam. The roofs of most coal seams (not bearing coal balls) contain animal remains which are characteristic of fresh and brackish waters (*Carbonicola, Anthracomya*, and *Naiadites*), showing that the forests which gave rise to these seams were submerged by an incursion of fresh or brackish water. Where, however, seams contain calcareous nodules the presence of marine fossils (*goniatites,*

more recently discovered in Russia, Moravia, Westphalia, Holland, United States of America, and New South Wales. Coal balls are particularly valuable, as, representing masses of fragments (not isolated remains), connections between the various plant organs can sometimes be made out.

(4) **The direct preservation of hard parts** is exemplified among plants by the numerous remains of calcareous algæ and the siliceous valves of diatoms. The bones and shells of animals are often preserved with little or no chemical change.

Incrustation, mummification, and the direct preservation of hard parts are common to both plant and animal fossils, but the petrification of soft tissues is almost unknown in the animal kingdom, though in certain animals (e.g. corals) the hard parts may be preserved or may be replaced by minerals, thus retaining the minute structure. Incrustations usually afford the most convenient and satisfactory stratigraphical indices, and it is with these that we are mainly concerned.

B. THE COAL MEASURE AGE

Beyond the remains of algæ (and especially of calcareous algæ) little is known of the plant-life of the early Palæozoic, the Cambrian, Ordovician, and Silurian, though algæ no doubt existed from the pre-Cambrian onwards. Most of the strata laid down in these epochs, being deposited in salt water, would be little likely to include fossil remains of land plants, though primitive ferns and Lycopods must have existed in Silurian times. The earliest certainly known land floras were Devonian, and included ferns, Lycopods, and Pteridosperms (as well as the Psilophytales, algæ, fungi, and bacteria).

In the succeeding epoch, the Carboniferous, and especially in Coal Measure times, the ferns, Lycopodiales, Equisetales, and Pteridosperms underwent very great development (Plate I), and Conifers made their appearance.

The characteristic plants of the Mesozoic were Gymnosperms—the Cycadales, Ginkgoales, and Coniferales, accompanied by Mesozoic ferns. In the Cainozoic the Angiosperms (Dicotyledons and Monocotyledons) became dominant, their development being apparently related to that of the higher insects (bees, wasps, butterflies, and moths), many of which pollinated the flowers. Angiosperms developed suddenly at the end of the Jurassic, their advent constituting by far the greatest invasion of new forms in the history of the plant kingdom.

Aviculopecten, etc.) indicate that in these (comparatively few) cases the forest was submerged by an incursion of the sea. It was evidently from the sea water that the petrifying minerals were derived. *Any seam the roof of which contains marine shells should be carefully searched for seam and roof nodules.* The subject of "coal balls" has been investigated by Dr. M. C. Stopes and Professor D. M. S. Watson (*Phil. Trans. Roy. Soc. Lond.*, ser. B, vol. 200, 1909, p. 167), while a considerably simplified method of sectioning the nodules has been developed by Dr. J. Walton and Dr. R. Koopmans (*Nature*, vol. 122, 1928, p. 571).

The Coal Measure strata in Britain vary in thickness from 2,000 to 8,000 feet, and consist of clays, shales, sandstones, and coals. The included fossils, both plant and animal, indicate that the rocks were mainly deposited in fresh or brackish water (i.e. in a vast series of lakes or lagoons, or in estuaries). It is probable that during this age the earth's crust in North-West Europe underwent a slow and steady depression which kept pace with sedimentation and resulted in the formation of extensive badly drained land areas little above sea-level. On the swamps thus formed the innumerable plants, some of the remains of which went to form the coal seams, flourished, one forest succeeding another after intervals of depression and sedimentation. The exceptionally large number of plants preserved (encrusted in the shales and sandstones, mummified in coal, and petrified in "coal balls"), which was much greater than at any other period in the earth's history, does not necessarily imply an exceptionally luxuriant vegetation, as sometimes has been supposed. Since tissues rapidly decay in air, only those plants living in or near water have much chance of preservation as fossils. Probably nine out of every ten coal seams were formed of vegetable matter which accumulated where it grew—in or very near swamps. The wealth of fossil plants in the Coal Measures is thus adequately explained by the exceptional facilities available for their preservation in Upper Carboniferous times. The atmosphere probably contained about the same percentage of carbon dioxide as at present, and the climate was temperate and uniform over an extensive area for a very considerable period.

The British Coal Measures have been divided, on lithological grounds, into Upper, Middle, and Lower (excluding the "Millstone Grit"). These terms, however, were often used in a purely local sense, and the so-called Upper Coal Measures of one area may actually be of the same age as the "Middle" Coal Measures of another. On the basis of the fossil floras present at various levels in the rocks Dr. Kidston recognised the following divisions:

True Upper Coal Measures = RADSTOCKIAN SERIES* (Radstock Group, Keele Group).

Transition Coal Measures = STAFFORDIAN SERIES (Newcastle-under-Lyme Group, Etruria Marl Group, Blackband Group).

True Middle Coal Measures = YORKIAN (= Kidston's WESTPHALIAN) SERIES (including, in some districts, part of the "Millstone Grit").

True Lower Coal Measures = LANARKIAN SERIES (including, in some districts, part of the "Millstone Grit").

* Kidston divided the Radstockian Series into the Radstock, Farrington, and Keele Groups. The Farrington Series of Somerset, the type of the Farrington Group, has been shown by the writer to belong to the Keele Group (a reference with which Kidston himself agreed), so that the middle group must be omitted from the classification.

The characteristic assemblages of species by which the Radstockian, Staffordian, Yorkian, and Lanarkian Series may be recognised are dealt with in Chapter VIII.

The "Millstone Grit" is usually a coarse sandstone lying beneath the Coal Measures; its name is due to the fact that in East Lancashire and Yorkshire the rock was once used for grinding corn. In South Wales a massive sandstone occurs at the top of the "Millstone Grit," and is known to miners as "Farewell Rock," because no workable coals are found in or below it. The age of the "Millstone Grit," as shown by its fossil contents, varies in different parts of the country and at different levels in the same district. Around Bristol and in Pembrokeshire the topmost beds are of Yorkian age, while those beneath belong to the Lower Carboniferous. Around the Midlothian basin, on the other hand, the upper two-thirds of the Millstone Grit contain a Lanarkian and the lower third a Lower Carboniferous flora. In the Forest of Dean the "Millstone Grit" appears to be entirely of Lower Carboniferous age, and that in South Lancashire mainly or wholly belongs to the Upper Carboniferous.

C. *PLANT DIVISIONS IN THE COAL MEASURES*

A provisional outline classification of the plant kingdom, so far as groups mentioned in the following pages are concerned, is given on page 18. Groups which are known as fossils only are marked by an asterisk. Those groups of vascular (woody) plants which occur in the Coal Measures are printed in italics. (The various groups are not necessarily of equal value.)

The **Thallophytes** form the simplest great division of the plant kingdom. A thallus is a plant-body showing little or no differentiation of vegetative organs (roots, stems, and leaves), and therefore of functions, though certain of the more complex Thallophytes may have organs analogous to roots, stems, and leaves.

In the Thallophytes the sexual organs, where present, are usually very simple, consisting of more or less modified cells, and are often distributed over the entire body, not restricted to certain regions, as in higher groups. The Thallophytes contain no vascular tissue and are therefore, as a rule, obliged to inhabit wet or moist situations. The two main groups are the Algæ and the Fungi; the former, bearing green colouring matter (chlorophyll), are able to build up sugars, starches, etc., by the aid of sunlight, while the Fungi, lacking chlorophyll, live on the foodstuffs in other plants or animals (parasitic fungi) or on the matter formed by their partial decay (saprophytic fungi). The bacteria (Schizomycetes) form another non-green group of the division. Algæ,* fungi,† and bacteria have all been recognised in the Coal

---

* Professor E. G. Garwood has shown that the Lower Carboniferous calcareous algæ are diagnostic of horizons over wide areas.

† The higher fungi (Mushrooms and Toadstools) are unknown as true fossils, but the lower types (both saprophytic and parasitic) are known from the Coal Measures. Their

Measures, but they do not warrant further mention here beyond noting the importance of bacteria and fungi as agents of decay in the vegetable débris which eventually became coal. The Diatomaceæ (Bacillariaceæ), a somewhat isolated group of the Algæ, whose siliceous valves accumulated as oozes in both fresh and marine waters, are not known (beyond two Liassic species) from below the Cretaceous, though further research may reveal earlier forms.

The next great division of plants, the **Bryophytes,** includes the liverworts (*Hepaticæ*) and the mosses (*Musci*). These are mostly land plants, though, having no definite woody tissue, generally live in moist places. Compared with higher forms they are small and short-lived. They are characterised by a sharply marked alternation of generations (i.e. an alternation of sexless spore-producing individuals, "sporophytes," with sexed gamete-producing individuals, "gametophytes") and complex sexual organs (the flask-shaped archegonium containing the egg and the very uniform antheridium containing the sperms). The chief difference between the Bryophytes and the next division, the Pteridophytes, consists in the relative importance of the two generations: in Bryophytes the "plant" is the gametophyte generation; in Pteridophytes (and Spermatophytes) it is the sporophyte. The body of a liverwort is generally a thallus, but this sometimes forks and forms leaf-like extensions. The mosses show more differentiation of the plant body: they have leaf- and stem-like organs as well as rhizoids (hairs with the water-absorbing function of roots). The first and only undoubted examples of Palæozoic liverworts were obtained recently in the mummified condition by Dr. John Walton, who isolated the small specimens from fine Coal Measure shales by means of hydrofluoric acid. The mosses of the Coal Measures have proved equally elusive. Although many specimens have been described from time to time as moss remains, in most instances they bear such a strong resemblance to delicate branchlets of *Lycopodites, Selaginellites, Lepidodendron, Bothrodendron,* etc., as to leave considerable doubt whether they in fact represent mosses or other remains. The discovery of an undoubted fructification (capsule or sporogonium, representing the dependent sporophyte generation), either petrified in a "coal ball" or as an impression on shale, has yet to be made. Much more delicate tissues than those of moss capsules are preserved in "coal balls," and the fact that mosses grow in damp situations and in dense masses should have favoured their preservation as fossils. As Dr. Walton has pointed out, the best evidence for the existence of Palæozoic mosses is represented by *Muscites bertrandi* Lignier preserved in a siliceous nodule from the Stephanian of Grand-Croix near St-Étienne. The vegetative

---

threads (hyphæ) have been recognised in (1) stems of *Lepidodendron* (*Oochitrium lepidodendri*), and of *Lyginopteris* (*Zygosporites*), (2) leaves of *Cordaites borassifolius* (*Hysterites cordaitis* Grand 'Eury), leaves of *Sphenopteris neuropteroides* (*Excipulites callipteridis*), and as sub-epidermal diseases on leaves of *Neuropteris* as well as in the outer layers of roots, like the Mycorrhiza infecting the beech and other recent plants.

	Division	Example

THALLOPHYTES
   Algæ (including diatoms)   Seaweeds
   Fungi   Moulds
   Bacteria

BRYOPHYTES
   Liverworts   Marchantia
   Mosses   Bog Moss

NON-VASCULAR PLANTS

VASCULAR PLANTS

SPORE PLANTS

PTERIDOPHYTES
   Psilophytales*   Rhynia*
   Lycopodiales   Club Mosses
   *Sphenophyllales**   *Sphenophyllum**
   Equisetales   Horsetails
                         *Equisetites**
                         *Calamites**

   Filicales
     A. *Cœnopterideæ**   *Botryopteris**
        Ophioglossaceæ   Adder's Tongue
        Marattiaceæ   *Marattia*

    B. Filicineæ (homosporous)
        Osmundaceæ   Royal Fern
        Schizæaceæ, etc.   Tropical Ferns
        Cyatheaceæ   Tropical Tree Ferns
        Polypodiaceæ   Most Living Ferns

    C. Hydropteridineæ (heterosporous)   Pillwort

SEED PLANTS

SPERMATOPHYTES
   Gymnosperms
     *Pteridosperms**   *Lyginopteris*
                         Medullosa

     *Cordaitales**   *Cordaites*
     Cycadales   Cycads
     Bennettitales*   Bennettites
     Ginkgoales   Maidenhair Tree
     Coniferales   Pine, Yew, Larch
     Gnetales   Welwitschia

   Angiosperms
     Dicotyledons   Ash, Rose
     Monocotyledons   Grass, Palm

* Group known as fossils only. Group printed in *italics* occur in the Coal Measures.

organs only are preserved, but there can be little doubt as to the plant being a moss. *M. polytrichaceus* Renault and Zeiller, from the Stephanian, also almost certainly represents the remains of mosses.

The **Pteridophytes** formed a very large proportion of the Coal Measure flora. This is the simplest plant division possessing vascular tissues (within which water, dissolved salts and sugars, etc., are transported). By virtue of this vascular tissue the Pteridophytes are definitely land plants, and, as in the Spermatophytes, there is a marked differentiation of the vegetative organs with their corresponding functions. The sexual organs, archegonia and antheridia, of Pteridophytes are similar to those of the Bryophytes, and, as in that division, there is a marked alternation of generations. All living Pteridophytes are reproduced by means of unicellular spores (produced in cases called sporangia), but some extinct Pteridophytes, distinguished as the Lepidospermæ, bore seed-like fructifications (*Lepidocarpon* and *Miadesmia*). The Lycopodiales, including the club-mosses, were very common and widely distributed in Coal Measure times, while the Sphenophyllales, though comprising comparatively few species, were fairly common. The Equisetales, including the horsetails, were numerous throughout the period, and the Filicales, or ferns proper, were once thought to be profusely represented. In the Coal Measure period there were so many fern-*like* leaves that it was named the "Age of Ferns." It is now known, however, that many of these leaves belonged not to the ferns (which do not bear seeds) but to primitive seed-plants with similar foliage, the Pteridosperms.

The **Spermatophytes** comprise the Gymnosperms, with exposed seeds, and the Angiosperms, the seeds of which are protected by enclosure in a case, the ovary. No remains of Angiosperms have been recorded from the Coal Measures (a supposed Angiospermous stem recently recorded from America proved to be that of a Pteridosperm). Gymnosperms (in the broad sense), on the other hand, are represented by three groups, the Pteridosperms, the Cordaitales, and the Coniferales. The fern-like leaves of Pteridosperms are by far the commonest Coal Measure fossils. The Cordaitales, though less frequent, also left numerous impressions of leaves and seeds, but the Coniferales are very rarely found. They are a more advanced group than the Pteridosperms or the Cordaitales, and are commoner in later rocks. Detached Gymnospermous seeds which belong either to the Pteridosperms or the Cordaitales—it is usually impossible to determine which—are fairly frequently found as moulds, casts, or impressions.

Ferns and Pteridosperms are not only similar as regards their foliage: the microsporangia (pollen-sacs) of Pteridosperms have a general resemblance to the sporangia of ferns, and in both cases the reproductive organs occur directly on the leaves. The anatomical structure of the petioles and of the primary roots is similar, while there are certain similarities in stem structure. Besides the seeds borne, Pteridosperms have affinities with the Gymnosperms in the secondary thickening which occurs in both stem and root and in the double leaf-trace which leaves the stele.

Angiosperms show a great advance on Pteridosperms in the modification and segregation of the fertile parts (as well as in the root and stem anatomy and other features). The seeds and microsporangia of Pteridosperms were borne on leaves which were not or only slightly modified. There are also very considerable differences in structure between the primitive seeds of the Pteridosperms and the advanced seeds of the Angiosperms, and, whereas the wind-pollinated seeds of most Pteridosperms were probably shed from the plant so that further development occurred on the ground, in Angiosperms pollination (usually by insects), fertilisation, and embryo development, occur on the parent plant and the embryo enjoys a period of rest before being shed. The primitive seeds of Pteridosperms never, so far as is known, developed an embryo.

The comparatively sudden extinction of the Sphenophyllales, Pteridosperms, and Cordaitales, as well as of most of the Palæozoic Equisetales and Lycopodiales, at or about the end of the Permian epoch, constitutes one of the greatest changes in the history of plants, and calls for some far-reaching explanation. Only one Palæozoic group of Pteridophytes, the Filicales, has held its own through the successive floras until the present day. In the Northern Hemisphere we have evidence in the "red beds," developed locally at the top of the Coal Measures, of the inception of arid conditions, a conclusion which is also suggested by the appearance in stems of growth-rings (so-called annual rings), indicating a succession of distinctly marked seasons. The considerable development which took place in the Coal Measure floras was probably in the main due to the presence of adequate moisture, not only for growth but also for fertilisation. The extinction of so many Palæozoic plants under dry conditions was probably due to their dependence on free moisture for the completion of the act of fertilisation. (Angiosperms have overcome the critical period of fertilisation by passing the sperms to the egg in the pollen-tube.) In the Southern Hemisphere, the extinction of Palæozoic plants was even more complete than in the Northern, and is supposed to have resulted from the advent of glacial conditions.

We have now to examine in greater detail the main groups of vascular plants observable in the Coal Measures, namely, Lycopodiales, Sphenophyllales, Equisetales, Cordaitales, and (jointly, because, although belonging to different groups, their foliage was alike) the Pteridosperms and ferns. Before proceeding a note is necessary as to the connotation of the terms "genera" and "species" as applied to incrustations.

D. THE TERMS "GENERA" AND "SPECIES"

The fragmentary nature of incrustations necessitates separate generic names for roots, stems, leaves, and seeds which may have originally belonged to the same plant. Similarly, in a genus may be included organs which are superficially alike, but which originally belonged to widely different plants The basis of further classification is shape, size, external markings, etc., and such grouping is clearly artificial and provisional only. The reproductive organs constitute the most reliable basis of classification, and when plants are found in the fertile condition they are removed from the provisional "form" genus and placed in more satisfactory groups. Only in those cases where the external features (observed in incrustations), the internal structure (derived from petrifactions), and the form of the reproductive organs (from either form of preservation) are known is it possible fully and satisfactorily to compare a fossil plant with living types and so to give it a permanent place in a phylogenetic classification, i.e. one embodying true relationships, descent, and evolutionary tendencies.

At the same time there are many "species," as based on incrustations, whose systematic position is necessarily unsatisfactory, but which are of considerable stratigraphical value. Take, for example, *Annularia radiata*, impressions of leafy branches which are common in and characteristic of the Yorkian and Lanarkian Series. Several kinds of cones have been found attached to *A. radiata*, showing that it represents several distinct species. The fact that these leaves are seldom found with cones attached does not affect their value as zonal indices. The correlation of impressions with petrifactions also presents difficulties in certain instances. Stems which may show no constant structural differences are readily distinguished as impressions (e.g. *Lepidophloios, Lepidodendron aculeatum,* and *L. obovatum*).

It will be clear also that incrustation-species are often difficult to define, and the characters once thought to be distinctive may later be seen to be variable or to occur in another species. Transitions are occasionally found connecting two species and necessitating their union under the name by which they were first described. The union of species, however, should not be undertaken without convincing evidence, and if we are to err as between retaining too many or too few specific names the former is much to be preferred.

CHAPTER II

LYCOPODIALES

The Palæozoic Lycopodiales were mostly tree-forms: they were extremely abundant in Coal Measure times and a very considerable proportion of our coal seams consists of the wood and of the coats of the innumerable spores of these trees. The "flaming coals" especially contain large quantities of such spores.* The structure of the rootlets and the presence of aerating tissues in the stems, etc., as well as other features, leave little doubt that, for the most part, these plants grew in fresh or brackish water swamps. The small herbaceous Lycopodiales of the Coal Measures, designated *Lycopodites* Goldenberg and *Selaginellites* Zeiller,† were rare, although probably not so uncommon as has been thought, as in some cases they resemble and have probably been mistaken for leafy twigs of *Lepidodendron*, etc. It was from *Selaginellites* that the recent *Selaginella* (the Lesser Club-moss) descended. Most of the Palæozoic groups of the Lycopodiales became extinct about the end of that era, but some persisted into the Triassic.

Lepidodendron Sternberg includes trees similar in habit to, but much larger than, the recent club-mosses. They had a world-wide distribution in Carboniferous times and died out in the Permian. The trunks gradually tapered,

---

* In some cases coal seams can be identified and correlated by means of the spore content of the coals, spores with certain types of surface ornamentation predominating in certain seams and proving constant over wide areas (though other associated types, unrestricted in distribution, are useless). In an investigation of the Parkgate Seam by Miss M. M. Evans it was found that microspores were practically useless and megaspores were employed. R. Thiessen and J. N. Staud, however, have used microspores only, the results obtained being verified in several instances. Much work remains to be done in this direction.

Humic (= "bituminous," including ordinary house coals) appear to consist of bright and dull layers (actually representing the broken ends of lens-shaped masses) and the hard dull black portions, known as durain, when sectioned and examined under the microscope, are seen to be largely composed of the mummified spore-cases of Lycopods. Megaspores are, of course, the more conspicuous, but the matrix in which they are embedded consists largely of microspores. In the bright but not glassy layers (clarain) spores are scattered here and there, while in the bright glassy portions (vitrain) they occur only very occasionally.

A method of collecting and examining spores from bituminous shales (without sectioning) was developed by Mr. J. Bennie and Dr. Kidston (*Proc. Roy. Phys. Soc. Edinburgh*, vol. ix, 1886, p. 92).

† *Lycopodites* includes forms with the habit of recent club-mosses not known to be heterosporous (though the plants may have been heterophyllous); *Selaginellites* refers to heterosporous types. These plants occur as impressions only: although they are called "herbaceous," some may have developed secondary wood. In certain species the leaves were very thin, resembling the "leaves" of many recent mosses.

reaching well over 100 feet in height and two or more feet in girth. For a considerable distance above the ground the trunk remained unbranched, after which it forked, giving rise to branches which themselves repeatedly branched by forking (though the forks often developed unequally). The younger branches bore spirals of needle-shaped or linear leaves (*Lepidophyllum*), which, after persisting for some time, were shed, leaving their bases ("leaf-cushions") in oblique rows on the surface of the branch. The bark of mature *Lepidodendron* stems was thus clothed with diamond-shaped leaf-cushions lying transversely, on each of which was a rhomboidal leaf-scar, representing the actual point of attachment of the leaf. Just above the middle of the leaf-scar are three dot-like marks, the central being the point at which the vein (vascular bundle) passed from the stem into the leaf, and the two lateral ("parichnos") representing a strand of aerating (? occasionally secretory) tissue which was continuous in stem and leaf and which, during life, had an outlet to the air through two small openings below the leaf-scar.* Only in certain species of incrustations are the parichnos strands below the leaf-scar shown. Above and below the leaf-scar was usually a central ridge called the "keel," in some species bearing more or less characteristic transverse markings. A little above the centre of the leaf-scar a small triangular mark is observable: it is known as the "ligule scar"† and represents the pit in which the ligule was seated. For purposes of description the area of the leaf-cushion surrounding the leaf-scar is called the "field."

Before their true nature was known, imperfectly preserved stems of *Lepidodendron* were placed in separate "genera": *Bergeria* Sternberg, *Aspidiaria* Stur, and *Knorria* Sternberg thus represent stems which had reached various stages of decortication before fossilisation. In *Bergeria* the epidermis and sub-epidermal layers have been lost, so that, though the area of the leaf-cushions may (or may not) be shown, the leaf-scars are not preserved. In *Aspidiaria* we have casts of the stem at a deeper level in the cortex, while *Knorria* shows markings due to the tissues of the middle cortex. The peg-like ridges in the last-named represent pockets formed by the decay of a soft tissue which ensheathed each leaf-trace. All transitions may be found between these casts, which are of no botanical or geological value.

Lepidodendron acutum (Presl) (Plates III, *a*; IV, *a*; XX, *f*) is an earlier name for the *L. haidingeri* of Ettingshausen and of Zeiller. The slightly keeled leaf-cushions are vertically elongated, about 2 mm. wide by about

---

* When the small spiral shells known as *Spirorbis* are found on the bark of *Lepidodendron* most or all of the organisms occur on the infrafoliar parichnos scars. Professor Seward has suggested that they were attracted to this position by the escape of gases from the parichnos strands.

† The ligule is a small tongue-like organ with an enlarged base which, when present, always occurred in a deep flask-shaped cavity on the upper side of the leaf. The Lycopodiales are divided into (1) Eligulatæ (homosporous) (*Lycopodium, Plylloglossum, Lycopodites*), (2) Ligulatæ (heterosporous) (*Selaginella, Selaginellites, Lepidodendron, Sigillaria, Bothrodendron*, and *Isoetes*).

10 mm. long, and not prominent. A typical feature (separating the species at a glance from *L. ophiurus* and *L. simile*) is the fact that the leaf-scars occupy practically the whole width of the cushion, and if lines descend from their lateral angles they are very short. The leaves did not readily fall and often remain to obscure the form of the leaf-scars. The figure shows two or three leafy branches, and, on the right, a cone.

In *Lepidodendron lanceolatum* Lesqx. (Plates III, *b*; IV, *b*; XX, *a*) the leaves stand practically at right-angles to the stems, their apices being often slightly curved, and the broadest point (nearly 3 mm. across) occurring about half-way up the leaf. The leaf-scars are narrowly obovate or oblanceolate, open at the base, and emarginate. The ligule-scar is often clearly shown. There is a clear keel below the leaf-scar, which lacks markings of any kind, and the field is unmarked.

Lepidodendron aculeatum Sternb. (Plates III, *c*; XX, *b*) is a common and well-marked British species. The leaf-cushions are long compared with their width and are inflected at their upper and lower extremities. They are separated by a depressed area of the cortex and are not continuous above or below. Parichnos prints below the leaf-scar are clearly shown on each side of the keel. The leaf-scar occurs at about two-thirds up the cushion, and is at least as high as wide. The top of the leaf-cushion is keeled for about half of its distance only. Two lines descend from the angles of the leaf-scar, joining the margins of the leaf-base at about one-third of its height.

In *Lepidodendron ophiurus* Brongt. (Plates III, *d*; IV, *c*; XX, *c*) the leaf-cushions are shorter in proportion to their width than in *L. acutum* and they are more prominent. The keel is also more prominent, but is not crossed by transverse lines. The distinct leaf-scars situated at about two-thirds up the leaf-base are narrow, occupying only about one-third of its width at that point. Two lines descend from their lateral angles and continue to the base of the cushion, running close and parallel to the margins of the cushion. The leaves persisted for a long time: they are spreading at the base and then arched.

Lepidodendron simile Kidston (Plates III, *e*; IV, *d*; XX, *d*) is the *L. elegans* of Lindley and Hutton (*Fossil Flora*, vol. ii, pl. cxviii) and the *L. lycopodioides* of Zeiller (*non* Sternberg). The leaves were persistent on both this species and on the very similar *L. lycopodioides* Sternb., and the two are also similar in the characters of their leaf-bases. In Sternberg's plant, however, the leaves (expecially on the younger branches) are smaller and adpressed to the stem; in *L. simile* they are larger and spreading. The leaf-bases are not so prominent as in *L. ophiurus*; there is a keel which is more marked than in *L. acutum*, and which is usually ornamented with transverse lines seldom seen in *L. ophiurus*. The entire leaf-scar is never seen owing to the persistence of the leaves, but it occupies only about half the width of the cushion, and the lines which descend from its angles meet the margins of the cushion at about half-way. The upper angle of the leaf-scar is much more arched than in *L. ophiurus*.

Lepidodendron lycopodioides Kidston (? Sternb.) (Plates III, *f*; V, *a*; XX, *e*) has straight leaf-scars which are represented merely by an angular slit. Foliar prints are invisible, and the fusiform leaf-base bears an ornamented keel. The leaves lie close to the stem. On the larger stems the leaf-bases are somewhat similar to those of *L. simile*. Mr. Hemingway has evidence that the cone which Kidston described as belonging to *Bothrodendron minutifolium* was probably borne by this species.

Lepidodendron wortheni Lesqx. (Plates III, *g*; V, *b*; XX, *g*) bears leaf-cushions which are not longitudinally symmetrical. There is no keel and the field is traversed by numerous strong markings both above and below the leaf-scar. The upper and lower margins of the elliptical leaf-scar, which occupied the whole width of the cushion, are not clearly marked. The leaves persisted for a long time, and are more spreading and less arched than in *L. simile*.

Lepidodendron loricatum Arber (*pars*) (Plates III, *h*; XX, *h*) is the *L. dichotomum* of Zeiller (*non* Sternberg). Some authors have united the species to *L. obovatum*, but it is separated from that plant by its rhomboidal leaf-scars, which are higher (three-quarter way) up the cushions. Whereas in *L. obovatum* the foliar prints are on the lower portion of the scar, in *L. loricatum* they are in the middle. Again, the lines descending from the angles of the leaf-scar join the margin of the cushion more rapidly than in *L. obovatum*, and parichnos-scars are absent below the leaf-scar.

Lepidodendron obovatum Sternb. (Plates III, *i*; XXI, *e*) in many respects resembles *L. aculeatum*, but both the leaf-cushions and the leaf-scars are characteristically wider in proportion to their height. The keel above the leaf-scar is less clearly marked than in *L. aculeatum* and the transverse markings on the keel below the leaf-scar are fewer and fainter.

Lepidodendron rimosum Sternb. (Plates III, *j*; XXXVII, *f*) is readily recognised by the fact that the leaf-cushions, which are about three times as high as wide, are not contiguous but are separated by wide bands of cortex which bear more or less deep ridges. In this separation of the leaf-cushions it resembles *L. wedekindi* Weiss, but in *L. rimosum* the cortical ornamentation generally consists of irregular obliquely placed ridges, while in *L. wedekindi* the ridges run parallel with the leaf-scars and are clearly interlacing. *L. fusiforme* (Corda) (Plate VI, *c*) has contiguous leaf-cushions.

L. distans Lesqx. (= *L. serpentigerum* Koenig) (Plate VI, *a*) and *L. jaraczewski* Zeiller (Plate VI, *b*) are very distinctive and require no description here. *L. gaudryi* Renault (Plate VI, *d*) has elongated cushions surrounded by characteristic longitudinal lines. In *L. peachi* Kidston (Plate VI, *e*) both the cushions and scars are rhomboidal and a raised line joins their lateral angles. *L. landsburgi* Kidston (Plate VI, *f*) has a great resemblance to the Lower Carboniferous *L. veltheimianum* Sternb., and bears ulodendroid scars. The apices of the leaf-cushions twist in opposite directions and the bark between the cushions bears oblique irregular striæ. Two lines descend from the lateral angles of the scars and meet the margins of the cushions at about their middle.

Like *Lepidodendron*, the much rarer genus *Lepidophloios* Sternberg consists of tree-forms with forking branches bearing prominent rhomboidal leaf-cushions arranged in a spiral manner. While in the former genus the leaf-cushions are longer than broad, in the latter they are broader than long and are also overlapping. Again, in *Lepidodendron* the leaf-scar is usually situated just above the centre of the cushion, while in *Lepidophloios* it occurs at or very near the top. (Owing to the growth or collapse of underlying tissues, however, in this genus the scar may eventually appear to be at the lower end of the leaf-cushion.)

Lepidophloios laricinus Sternb. (Plates III, *k*; XXII, *i*) is easily distinguished from *L. acerosus* (L. and H.) (Plates III, *l*; XXII, *k*) by the leaf-cushions being two to three times as wide as high, whereas in the latter species they are rhomboidal, being little wider than high. A keel is scarcely shown in *L. laricinus*, but it is a prominent feature of *L. acerosus*.

Bothrodendron Lindley and Hutton (= *Cyclostigma* Haughton, usually reserved for the older and especially Upper Devonian species) covers a small group of tree-forms with a habit similar to that of *Lepidodendron*. While the young branchlets may bear indications of leaf-cushions, they are absent from the adult stems. On the branches are characteristically small oval or rhomboidal leaf-scars situated at some distance from each other, and containing the three point-like marks as in *Lepidodendron* and *Lepidophloios*. Above each leaf-scar is the small ligule-pit. Those leaves of *Bothrodendron* which have been recognised were small and broadly lanceolate with a single central vein. The fructifications consisted of cones whose position on the tree varied in different species; in general appearance these cones were similar to *Lepidostrobus*, though the sporangia were not radially elongated.*

The "paper coal" of Toula in Central Russia is composed of the cuticles of *Bothrodendron* stems.

Bothrodendron minutifolium (Boulay) (Plates V, *c*; XXII, *h*). The figure shows part of an old stem. On younger branches the leaf-cushions are elongated and bear transverse wrinkles; on old branches, such as the one figured, the leaf-scars are distant, being separated by areas of bark which bear undulating transverse grooves and narrow ridges with a pitted surface. The leaves were 5 mm. long and were soon shed from the stems. In the rarer *B. punctatum* L. and H. (Plate III, *m*), found in the Yorkian and the Lanarkian Series, the wrinkles are vertical and the leaf-scars seldom well preserved. This species is sometimes found in the Ulodendroid condition.

Asolanus Wood, once thought to be related to *Sigillaria*, is now regarded as being nearer to *Lepidodendron* or *Bothrodendron*. So far one species only has been recognised, *A. camptotænia* (Plates III, *n*; XXI, *c*). The leaf-scars are spirally arranged, and, whereas in *Sigillaria* there are three small prints on the leaf-scar, in *Asolanus* there is a circular print within which may be one or two small point-like scars. The bark between the leaf-bases often bears oblique lines. The scars are about 6·5 mm. wide by 2·5 mm. high. Decorticated stems of *Sigillaria* show curved scars in pairs (the parichnos); those of *Asolanus* show a single linear scar (the leaf-trace).

Pinakodendron Weiss represents stems similar to those of *Bothrodendron*, but differing in the shape of the leaf-scars and in the bark being ornamented

---

* Dr. Kidston regarded *Lepidostrobus olryi* Zeiller as the cone of *Bothrodendron minutifolium*, and in *L. olryi* the sporangia are radially elongated. Mr. Hemingway, however, who collected the specimens, believes that Kidston attributed this cone to *B. minutifolium* in error and that it belongs to *Lepidodendron lycopodioides*. The matter requires further investigation.

by a fine network of raised lines. In *P. macconochiei* Kidston (Plates III, *o*; XXIV, *e*) the oval leaf-scars are distant, about 2 mm. high by 1·5 mm. broad. Small ridges form a very fine irregular network on the bark.

Sigillaria Brongniart was widely distributed in the Carboniferous, but less so than *Lepidodendron*. It was a large group of trees which, in marked contrast to *Lepidodendron*, very rarely branched and usually had no true leaf-cushions. Some Sigillarias were tall and slender, attaining a height of about 100 feet; others were short, squat, and barrel-shaped with a domed apex. While the bark was usually longitudinally ribbed (*Eu-Sigillariæ*), it was sometimes smooth (*Sub-Sigillariæ*). The leaves, which were often indistinguishable from those of *Lepidodendron*, persisted for two or three years, and, on falling, left a vertical series of (usually) hexagonal leaf-scars. As in *Lepidodendron*, etc., each leaf-scar bears, a little above the middle, three point-like prints, while the ligule-pit can often be seen just above the leaf-scar. Between adjacent leaf-scars, especially near each scar, the bark may bear characteristic markings which aid in distinguishing species, while from each of the lateral angles of the leaf-scar, and especially where these are strongly marked, a line may descend. Certain decorticated stems of *Sigillaria* are referred to *Syringodendron* Sternberg. The leaves were, in some species, linear-lanceolate, but they generally cannot be referred to their parent plants and are therefore grouped with similar leaves belonging to *Lepidodendron*, etc., in the form-genus *Lepidophyllum*. Other common Sigillarian leaves were long and grass-like and are often called "grass" by miners: these are placed in the genus *Sigillariophyllum*. *Sigillaria* has been divided into four groups according to the stem being smooth or ribbed and the distance apart of the leaves—*Rhytidolepis* Sternberg, *Favularia* Sternberg, *Clathraria* Brongniart, and *Leiodermaria* Goldenberg, but the groups are of doubtful value. The fructifications of *Lepidodendron* and *Sigillaria* are usually found detached: those of the latter genus, where recognisable as such, are placed in *Sigillariostrobus* Schimper. They consist of cylindrical cones which occupy different positions on the plant in different species. Though generally occurring on large unbranched stems, they sometimes terminated the slender branchlets, as was usual in *Lepidodendron* and *Lepidophloios*. Some were 30 or more cm. in length and 3–5 cm. in diameter. *Sigillaria* bore two sizes of spores, "microspores" and "megaspores." The ripe cones were shed from the tree, their original position, when borne on the stem, being marked by oblong scars.

Ulodendron Lindley and Hutton (Plate XXI, *f*) is a "genus" in which are placed stems up to about a foot in diameter, bearing leaf-scars of *Bothrodendron punctatum*, leaf-cusions of *Lepidodendron*, and in some cases, according to Kidston, Sigillarian leaf-scars, and on each side of the stem a vertical row of large circular cup-shaped umbilicate depressions. The umbilicus is central in *Lepidodendron* and eccentric in *Bothrodendron*. The cup-shaped depressions were originally thought to be due to the pressure of sessile or shortly stalked cones against the branch which bore them. They are now recognised as scars left by certain smaller leafy branches which were shed. Occasionally the cast of an isolated scar is found.

Halonia Lindley and Hutton (Plate **XXXIX**, *a*), consisting of detached branches which are up to 7 or 8 cm. in diameter, bears scars or knobs, usually in spirals. The leaf-cushions, where present, show that the specimens mostly belonged to *Lepidophloios*, though some were possibly Lepidodendroid. Kidston regarded them as representing cone-bearing branches of *Lepidophloios* and the knobs as the bases of the stalks of cones which were shed. It is now known, however, that the cones of *Lepidophloios*, like those of *Lepidodendron*, were borne at the ends of the slender branches and not on the thicker Halonial branches, and the latter were evidently leafy branches.

Sigillaria ovata Sauveur (Plates **VII**, *a*; **XIX**, *i*) and *S. lævigata* Brongt. (Plates **VII**, *b*; **XXII**, *j*) are somewhat similar. In *S. ovata*, however, the leaf-scars are oval and more closely placed than in *S. lævigata*, where they are hexagonal. In the latter species the two lateral angles of the scars give rise to descending lines which are absent from *S. ovata*. Again, in *S. ovata* fine markings occur beneath the scars, such ornamentation being absent from *S. lævigata*. *S. cordigera* Zeiller (Plates **VII**, *c*; **XIX**, *h*) is characterised by heart-shaped scars and a smooth bark.

Sigillaria sauli Brongt. (Plates **VII**, *d*; **XIX**, *j*) has straight or slightly flexuous furrows. The leaf-scars are separated vertically by 1–1·5 cm., and vary from sub-hexagonal to oval. They occupy almost the whole width between the ribs and are surmounted by a strong curved line which is as wide as the scar itself. The bark is smooth.

S. cumulata Weiss (Plates **VII**, *e*; **XIX**, *g*), a Radstockian species, was once confused by Kidston with *S. tessellata*, common in the Yorkian. The furrows are strongly marked, about 6 mm. apart, and the elliptical leaf-scars occupy their whole width. Above and below, the leaf-scars are contiguous. They are half as high as wide.

Sigillaria elongata Brongt. (Plates **VII**, *f*; **XIX**, *e*) resembles *S. rugosa* Brongt. (Plates **VII**, *h*; **XXI**, *a*), but is distinguished from that species by the scars being closer together and by their being surmounted by a little arc. Lines descend from the lateral angles of the scar in both species, but those in *S. elongata* are much shorter. The most characteristic feature of *S. elongata*, however, is the longitudinally extended leaf-scar which is almost elliptical. *S. elongata* also differs from *S. deutschiana* (Plates **VII**, *g*; **XIX**, *f*) in its longer scars and in the lateral descending lines being shorter. *S. kinletensis* Arber has points of resemblance with both *S. elongata* and *S. rugosa*. The scars are closer and more elongated than in *S. rugosa* and the ornamentation of the bark between the scars is distinctive. *S. kinletensis* bears many curved closely placed wrinkles, but there is no plume-like mark above the scar. It differs from *S. elongata* in the scar having a more pointed apex, in the ornamentation, and in the foliar prints being situated higher up the scar.

In *S. deutschiana* the descending lines go to the scar below. This species is most like *S. rugosa*, but the scars are shorter, almost pentagonal, and little higher than wide. There are no fine plume-like lines above the scar (such as occur in *S. rugosa*).

Sigillaria mammillaris Brongt. (Plates VII, *i*, *j*; XIX, *c*) is characterised by prominent and closely placed leaf-scars which are obliquely truncated (distinguishing the species from *S. elegans*—Plates VII, *k*; XXI, *d*). The scars are closer than in *S. scutellata* (Plates VII, *l*; XIX, *d*). In the last-named species they are shorter than in *S. elongata* and occupy more of the width of the ribs, while the lines descending from their lateral angles diverge more. The descending lines in *S. scutellata* are clearer than in *S. mammillaris*, but both species are subject to variation.

Sigillaria trigona (Sternb.) (Plates VII, *m*; XIX, *a*) is a well-marked species. The furrows are distinctly zigzagged and the leaf-scars pear-shaped, the contraction occurring in the upper half. Adjacent scars are separated by a small transverse furrow, which may be straight or curved. The areas on which the leaf-scars occur are smooth. The species differs from *S. mammillaris* in the latter having straight or only slightly flexuous furrows and in the shape of the leaf-scars.

Sigillaria candollei Brongt. (Plates VII, *n*; XIX, *b*) has straight convex ribs, 10–12 mm. wide. The oval leaf-scars are about 10 mm. long by 5 mm. broad, and are separated vertically by about 20 mm. Usually above and below the leaf-scar there are fairly strong oblique markings: these are not so strong as in *S. rugosa* (which also has a plume-like mark above the scar, and in which the lateral angles are more prominent).

Sigillaria tessellata Brongt. (Plates VII, *o*; XXI, *b*) differs from *S. mammillaris* in the ribs being almost straight and unornamented. The leaf-scars are nearly contiguous and occupy about two-thirds the width of the ribs. From *S. davreuxi* Brongt. (Plates VII, *p*; XXXVIII, *f*) it differs in the shorter and less prominent scars. In *S. davreuxi*, also, the transverse line above the scar is always definitely curved. *S. elegans* (Sternb.) (Plates VII, *k*; XXI, *d*) is distinguished from *S. tessellata* by the zigzag course of the ribs, and the transverse lines separating the scars do not reach the furrows. The scars are often higher than wide in *S. elegans*.

Sigillaria elegans differs from *S. tessellata* and *S. mammillaris* by the distinctly zigzag course of the furrows. The transverse lines on the ribs separating the scars do not reach the furrows. Although the scars are often higher than wide, they are not so high (compared with their width) as in *S. mammillaris*, are closer together, and no transverse wrinkles occur below them.

Sigillaria discophora Koenig (Plate XXI, *f*) is the *Ulodendron minus* of Lindley and Hutton. Owing to the persistence of the leaves the leaf-scars are seldom seen, but Kidston recorded an example of the species which bore the usual three foliar prints, and referred the species to *Sigillaria*. The size of the Ulodendroid scars is of no specific value.

Sigillaria boblayi Brongt. (Plates VII, *q*; XXXVIII, *e*) resembles *S. davreuxi* Brongt., but the leaf-scars are larger and wider in proportion to their height, while their lateral angles are more prominent. *S. boblayi* has also some resemblance to *S. scutellata*, but the scars are larger and less close and are surmounted by a clearly marked arc. The species is generally larger than *S. mammillaris*. *S. davreuxi* stands nearer to *S. tessellata*, but is distinguished by the longer leaf-scars beneath which wrinkles are borne.

Sigillaria essenia Achepohl (Plates VII, *r*; XXI, *g*) has affinities with *S. ovata*, and was united to that species by Zeiller. Whereas in *S. ovata* the leaf-scars are generally higher than wide, in *S. essenia* they are rather wider than high, and, whereas in *S. ovata* the bark is practically smooth below the scar (there are occasionally very fine lines), in *S. essenia* distinct transverse lines occur.

Sigillaria principis Weiss (Plates VII, *s*; XXXVII, *b*) is distinguished from *S. lævigata* (in which the lines descending from the lateral angles of the leaf-scar are similar) by its narrower ribs, closer scars, by the presence of an arc surmounting each scar, and by the occurrence of an ornamentation of fine lines on the surface of the ribs between the scars.

S. strivelensis Kidston (Plate VIII, *a*) is known from the Lanarkian Series. The furrows undulate and the leaf-scars are pentagonal with a notch on the upper margin and surmounted by fine plume-like marks. Three series of transverse striæ descend from the base of the scar and diverge in their course to the scar below. This species stands nearest to *S. polyploca* Boulay (Plate VIII, *b*), but the latter lacks the plume-like markings, has a different ornamentation below the scar, and the lines descending from the lateral angles of the scar are longer.

S. incerta Kidston (Plate VIII, *c*), another Lanarkian species, is difficult to separate from *S. elegans*. It has strongly zigzagged furrows. The hexagonal cushion has a slightly notched upper margin, sharp lateral angles, and a pointed or rounded base. It differs from the somewhat similar *S. brardi* Brongt. (Plate VIII, *d*), which is unknown from the Lanarkian, in that in *S. incerta* the lateral angles of the leaf-scar touch the margins of their cushion above its lateral angles. In *S. brardi* the lateral angles of scars and those of the cushions coincide. *S. semipulvinata* Kidston (Plate VIII, *e*) bears rhomboidal leaf-scars which occupy the top of the leaf-cushion, the upper margin flat or slightly notched, the lower rounded and the lateral angles being sharp. *S. sol* Kidston (Plate VIII, *m*) is a very rare Yorkian form in which the furrows are straight, 2·5 cm. wide, bearing leaf-scars 1·2 cm. wide by 1·0 cm. high. The ornamentation above the scar is very distinctive. *S. arzinensis* Corda (Plate VIII, *f*) is probably the *S. ovalis* Lesqx. It has straight furrows bearing oval leaf-scars 5 mm. broad by 7 mm. high and separated vertically by about 2·5 cm. From the fairly distinct lateral angles two short lines descend. Markings may occur on the ribs, but they do not appear to be distinctive.

In *Sigillaria nudicaulis* Boulay (Plate VIII, *g*) the furrows are straight and the oval leaf-scars 3–5 cm. apart in the vertical direction. Their upper margin is slightly emarginate and short lines may or may not descend from the lateral angles. Ornamentation may be absent from the ribs and in any case is observable only by the aid of a lens: when present, irregular lines occur above the ligule-pit, a few transverse striæ below the scar and beneath these faint longitudinal striations. *S. transversalis* Brongt. (Plate VIII, *h*) has furrows which may undulate slightly, the ribs being about 1 cm. wide and the distance between successive leaf-scars about 1·5 cm. The scars are 9–12 mm. across by 6 or 7 mm. high, occupying from three-fifths to the whole width of the rib. In the narrower type short lines leave the lateral angles and pass to the ribs. A transverse furrow occurs above the ligule-pit. In *S. transversalis* var. *sparsifolia* Boulay the scars are more distant, relatively narrower, and higher. The ribs may be smooth or marked by fine longitudinal and transverse striæ.

Sigillaria pringlei Kidston (Plate VIII, *i*) has some resemblance to *S. reniformis* Brongt. (Plate VIII, *j*), but the scars are smaller (5 mm. wide by 3 mm. high in the former, 7 mm. wide by 6 mm. high in the latter) with more marked lateral angles. In *S. pringlei* they are separated by a vertical distance of 3·5 cm., and in *S. reniformis* by 1–2 cm. *S. reniformis* not only has a transverse line above the ligule-pit (absent from *S. pringlei*), but the area below the scar is divided into three longitudinal areas by lines which descend from the lateral angles and from the base of the scar. *S. reticulata* Lesqx. (Plate VIII, *k*) is a non-ribbed *Sigillaria*. The leaf-scars in adjacent rows alternate and are separated vertically by from 7 to 30 mm. The scars are generally broader than high (4–6 mm. broad by 3–4 mm. high). The upper margin is distinctly notched, the lower rounded. Beneath the scar faint transverse lines may occur and the ribs bear fairly short slightly undulating lines. *S. punctirugosa* Kidston (Plate VIII, *l*) has straight furrows about 5 mm. apart bearing pentagonal scars separated by about 13 mm., occupying the whole width of the rib. Two rows of slightly diverging lines occur beneath the scar, passing to the transverse line which surmounts the scar next below. The ribs are ornamented by numerous fine dots.

 S. micaudi Zeiller (Plate VIII, *n*) is a Yorkian species with straight or slightly undulating furrows. The leaf-scars are about 1 cm. apart and occupy about three-fifths of the ribs, measuring about 6 cm. high by 7 cm. broad. Above the ligule-pit is a strongly marked ridge and below the scar are two series of diverging lines passing to the scar next below. The lateral angles of the scars are prominent and sharp. *S. meachemi* Arber is very similar to *S. micaudi*. In Zeiller's species, however, the lateral angles of the leaf-scar are sharp and the lower margin slightly concave, while in Arber's both are rounded. *S. nortonensis* Crookall (Plate VIII, *o*) has straight ribs which are 10–12 mm. apart. The vertical distance between successive scars is 20 mm. The scars are oval-hexagonal, slightly emarginate above, 8–9 mm. wide, 7 mm. high. Above the ligule-pit is a transverse line. The foliar cicatricules occur a little above the middle of the scar. *S. kidstoni* Crookall (Plate VIII, *p*) has slightly flexuous ribs 23–25 mm. apart, scars separated by 12–20 mm., 6–9 mm. wide, 3–4½ mm. high, lateral angles rounded, upper margin emarginate, lower rounded. A transverse line occurs above some of the scars. Transverse wrinkles occur beneath the scar and extend in a vertical file almost to the scar below. This species stands nearest to *S. reniformis* in the form of the scar, but is readily distinguished by the ornamentation of the ribs as well as by the shape of the scars.

 Lepidophyllum Brongniart includes leaves, both sterile and fertile, of a number of the Lycopodiales which, being found detached, cannot be referred to their parent plants. Some were short and more or less lanceolate, while others were up to 20 cm. or so in length and grass-like. Both types possessed a single vein running down the centre.

 Lepidophyllum triangulare Zeiller (Plates IX, *j*; XXII, *d*) consists of a wedge-shaped lower portion 5–8 mm. long whose greatest width is about 4 mm., and a triangular upper portion whose two lateral angles descend somewhat. This measures 12–15 mm. in length and 8–12 mm. in breadth, and has a sharp apex. There is a single central vein. The whole bract resembles an arrow-head.

 Sigillariophyllum Grand 'Eury is represented by the common grass-like leaves, *S. bicarinatum* (L. and H.) (Plate XXXV, *b*), originally thought to have two veins. There is actually a single central vein, and the appearance of double veins is due to small grooves, one of which ran on each side of the vein. These grooves contained the stomata: they filled with carbonaceous matter during fossilisation. Such leaves have been found attached to several species of Sigillarian stems and possibly also occurred on some examples of *Lepidodendron.*

Lepidostrobus Brongniart includes the fructifications belonging to *Lepidodendron, Lepidophloios, Bothrodendron,* and possibly to some species of *Sigillaria.* (It is significant that stems of the last-named genus showing rounded or angular cone-scars, though not common, are more frequent than Sigillarian cones, recognised as such.) The cones were usually cylindrical, but sometimes ovoid, and large specimens exceeded 30 cm. in length by 5 cm. in diameter. Average examples measured 7–15 cm. long by 1·5 cm. in diameter. They consisted of a central stalk with crowded spirals of bracts (sporophylls), the upper surface of each of which bore a single radially elongated sporangium. It is probable that most, if not all, the arborescent Palæozoic Lycopods bore two kinds of spores, small (microspores) and large (megaspores or macrospores). Where both kinds of spore occurred in the same cone the larger are found in the lower part of the cone and the smaller in the upper.* In the genus *Lepidodendron* stalked cones were usually situated at the ends of the smaller leafy branches. Secondary wood is generally absent from the steles of Lepidostrobi, and it has been suggested that this is an indication that the ripe cones were shed and that fertilisation occurred on the damp ground.

Lepidostrobus minus (Goode) (Plates IX, *c*; XXII, *a, b*) represents (usually) detached sporophylls which have the general form of arrow-heads and are very similar to (but smaller than) *Lepidophyllum triangulare,* described above. *Lepidostrobus lanceolatus* (L. and H.) (Plates IX, *f*; XXII, *c*) also consists of (usually) detached sporophylls, each with a single central vein, but in this species the upper portion of the organ is lanceolate, 3–5 cm. long and 6–9 mm. wide. The apex is sharply pointed. Except in point of size, *L. lanceolatus* does not greatly differ from *L. majus* (Brongt.) (Plate IX, *k*).

Sigillariostrobus rhombibracteatus Kidston (Plate XXII, *g*) is a long cylindrical stalked cone from which the bracts readily became detached. The latter were rhomboidal with a sharp apical point, and had fine marginal hairs. The cone was probably heterosporous, but megaspores only have been found as yet. *Sigillariostrobus nobilis* Zeiller occurs rarely in Britain (Staffordian and Yorkian Series) and in France. The cylindrical cones reach 30 cm. or more in length and 5 to 6 cm. in breadth with an axis 1·0 cm. across. The spreading imbricated bracts are lanceolate, 2·5–3·0 cm. long and 0·8 cm. broad, with a long sharp point. As in other species of *Sigillariostrobus,* the bracts were deciduous. In *S. ciliatus* Kidston, a Yorkian species, the linear-lanceolate bracts are sharply pointed and bear marginal hairs. Kidston has pointed out that his *Lepidostrobus spinosus* ("Cone oblong, and tapering to

---

* Some cones, closely related to *Lepidostrobus,* developed seed-like organs (*Lepidocarpon*), as did at least one of the herbaceous Palæozoic Lycopods (*Miadesmia*).

its blunt apex; bracts lanceolate, acute, single-veined, adpressed, rigid; external extremities of sporangia rhomboidal") and *L. squarrosus* (= the *L. variabilis* of Schimper and Zeiller, but differing from the commoner but ill-defined *L. variabilis* L. and H. in its larger size and laxer spreading bracts) may belong to *Sigillariostrobus*. The stem of the former was stout and erect and, as Kidston showed, suggests that the fructification was produced from the side of a stem and was not pendent from the delicate branchlets. *L. spinosus* and *L. squarrosus* are very rare, the former occurring in the Radstockian, Yorkian, and Lanarkian Series, but the latter being confined to Lanarkian rocks.

Stigmaria Brongniart is the name given to the rhizophore* of *Lepido-dendron*, *Sigillaria*,† and probably of *Lepidophloios* and *Bothrodendron*. *Stigmaria* is therefore the commonest and most widely distributed fossil of the Coal Measures, occurring especially in the clays which lie immediately beneath most coal seams (and very probably representing the old muddy soils on which the Coal Measure forests flourished). Erect specimens are often to be met with and the position of the rootlets shows that in many cases they are exactly where the tree originally grew. Representing as they do the underground parts of a large number of distinct species belonging to several genera, *Stigmaria* has no stratigraphical value. The fossils occur as cylindrical moulds and casts (very rarely as pith-casts), complete examples spreading downwards from the base of the tree trunk, which may be 3 or 4 feet in diameter, into four main branches; each branch generally forks three times, giving in all sixteen ultimate branches. In irregular spirals on the surface are circular scars marking the points at which lateral rootlets were given off; each well-preserved scar shows a central pit representing the position of the vascular bundle, while the space between this and the circumference of the scar represents the broad soft cortex of the rootlet. The rootlets were 40 cm. or more long and up to 1·5 cm. in diameter; they spread out in all directions and ramified in the soil and in the humus formed by the decay of previous generations of plants.

Stigmaria minuta Goeppert pro var. (Plate XXII, *e*) was originally described as a variety of the common *S. ficoides* (Sternb.) (Plate XXII, *f*), but is distinguished from it by the very small elliptical scars (1–3 mm. in diameter), and by the outer surface of well-preserved examples being very finely granular. *S. minuta* has the smallest rootlet-scars of any described *Stigmaria*. *S. ficoides* var. *minor* Geinitz is a small and rare form of the common species, while the bark of *S. ficoides* var. *undulata* Goepp. bears undulating

---

* Dr. Scott has pointed out that the organ does not correspond exactly with a root, rhizome or rhizophore, and that in these early groups of vascular plants the distinction between root and shoot is less clear than in more advanced types.

† The rhizophore of some species of *Sigillaria* (probably of the non-ribbed types) is placed in the genus *Stigmariopsis* Grand 'Eury. The organ is shorter and thicker than in *Stigmaria*, and the bark bears an irregular network of lines. Pith-casts of *Stigmariopsis* are ribbed like those of *Calamites*, but show no nodes. While *Stigmaria* is very common in the Coal Measures, *Stigmariopsis* is very rare.

lines passing longitudinally between the rootlet-scars. *S. eveni* Lésqx. also bears longitudinal lines, but they are short and much less regular than in *S. ficoides* var. *undulata*, while the rootlet-scars are small (rarely more than 3 mm. in diameter) and irregularly placed. In *S. reticulata* Goepp. pro var. the bark bears a meshwork of lines. This may represent a state of preservation of *S. ficoides*.

Omphalophloios White is represented by a single species, *O. anglicus* (Sternb.), occurring fairly rarely in the Radstockian Series only. It probably represents the rhizophore of a Lycopod. Specimens resemble *Lepidodendron* (in which genus they were first placed) in the cortex being divided into rhomboidal cushions. The cushions, however, are not keeled and the scars borne on them are distinct both from those of *Lepidodendron* and *Stigmaria*. The circular or oval (? rootlet) scar is situated about two-thirds up the cushion and has a central vascular cicatrice. Just below it is a small raised triangular area which contains a small pit.

CHAPTER III

SPHENOPHYLLALES

OF the Sphenophyllales* we need to deal with the single genus *Sphenophyllum* which became extinct in the Palæozoic. It has no near relationship with any known group of plants, unless it be with the recent Psilotaceæ.†

Sphenophyllum Brongniart was herbaceous and relatively small, consisting of a slender pithless stem up to 1·5 cm. broad and bearing at the somewhat swollen nodes whorls of wedge-shaped, deeply divided or linear leaves. It is very probable that the slender stem of *Sphenophyllum* was unable to bear the weight of its leaves and that the plant obtained support from the surrounding vegetation, i.e. that is was a "scrambler." As has been frequently pointed out, in habit and general appearance it must have closely resembled the "cleavers" or "goosegrass" (*Galium aparine*) of our hedgerows, but this is, of course, a purely superficial resemblance, *Sphenophyllum* being a Pteridosphyte and "goosegrass" a dicotyledon.

Certain of the nodes of *Sphenophyllum* gave off a single lateral branch. The internodes, which varied in length from 0·5 to 3 or more cm., were traversed by longitudinal ribs. These ribs passed straight through the nodes and the leaves of adjacent whorls of leaves were superposed (contrast *Calamites*). The leaves occurred in multiples of three; their bases were separate, not fusing to form a small collar round the stem (contrast *Annularia*). In some species of *Sphenophyllum* the leaves varied in shape on the same plant, the larger branches tending to bear undivided (entire) leaves and the smaller to bear leaves which were more or less deeply cleft from the apex towards the base. The plants were thus often heterophyllous. A similar feature occurs in the Water Crowfoot (*Ranunculus aquatilis*) and other recent aquatic species, and, on this account, *Sphenophyllum* has been regarded as an aquatic plant. It has been pointed out, however, that both entire and divided leaves may occur on the same branch irregularly (and especially on the fertile branches)

---

* Provisionally included in the Sphenophyllales are (1) *Cheirostrobus* (a very complex cone, structurally preserved, from the Calciferous Sandstones of Pettycur) and (2) *Pseudobornia* (impressions of jointed stems bearing four leaves at each node and lax cones, from the Upper Devonian of Bear Island).

† The Psilotaceæ include *Psilotum* (tropical) and *Tmesipteris* (an epiphyte on tree-ferns in Australia and New Zealand).

and that the relatively thick stele and absence of aerating tissues do not suggest an aquatic habit. On the other hand, the thin stem, the central position of the wood, and the large diameter of the conducting elements (xylem and phlœm) are features of climbing plants.

Those leaves of *Sphenophyllum* which had broad apices bore a number of teeth, rounded in some species and sharp in others. One or two veins, according to the species, passed from the stem into the base of the leaf. In traversing the leaf blade, the veins forked repeatedly until finally a single veinlet passed to each apical tooth (or, where the leaf was much divided, to each segment). (In *Annularia* and *Asterophyllites* the leaves had a single vein which did not fork.)

The fructifications of *Sphenophyllum* consisted of long narrow cones which occurred either as lateral branches or at the ends of the leafy stems. They reached 12 cm. in length and 1·2 cm. in diameter. These cones were composed of numerous modified leaves ("bracts" or "sporophylls") whose bases fused to form a collar round the cone-axis. The sporangia were borne on the upper surface of some or all of the bracts, their position varying in different species. Although in one species, *S. verticillatum*, two kinds of sporangia occur, megaspores have not yet been observed, and, as far as is known, *Sphenophyllum* was homosporous. Impressions of the cones of *Sphenophyllum* may be superficially very similar to those of the fossil Equisetales, but their structure was quite distinct.

Sphenophyllum emarginatum Brongt. (Plates X, *a*; XXIII, *c*) has whorls of leaves which are 5–10 mm. long and 2·5–7 mm. broad at the apex. The edges are straight (contrast *S. cuneifolium* and *S. saxifragæfolium*) and the apex bears six to twelve teeth which are always rounded. There are one or two veins at the base of the leaf. The cone of this species was described by Weiss as *Bowmanites germanicus*.

Sphenophyllum majus (Bronn) (Plates X, *c*; XXIII, *f*) bears longer leaves (12–20 or more mm.). Though sometimes entire at the apex, they are usually divided by one or three clefts. (Only the larger leaves of *S. emarginatum* are cleft.) The apex bears eight to sixteen sharp or obtuse teeth, which are pointed rather than triangular. Two veins enter the leaf.

Sphenophyllum cuneifolium (Sternb.) (Plates X, *b*; XXIII, *g*) has leaves of about the same size as *S. emarginatum*: the edges are straight or slightly concave outwards, and the undivided apex is characterised by six to twelve sharp triangular teeth.

Sphenophyllum saxifragæfolium (Sternb.) (Plates X, *d*; XXIII, *a*, *b*), about the same size as the preceding, has leaf margins which are clearly concave outwards, and the apex is divided by one, three, or five clefts. A single vein enters the leaf in *S. cuneifolium* and *S. saxifragæfolium*.

Sphenophyllum myriophyllum Crépin (Plates X, *e*, *f*; XXIII, *d*) bears leaves which are from 10 to 30 mm. long, divided by one or three clefts reaching almost to the base. One or two veins enter the base of the leaf. The foliage of *S. trichomatosum* Stur (Plates X, *g*; XXIII, *e*) consists of narrow forking segments. It is a commoner plant than *S. myriophyllum*, with which it has sometimes been confused. *Sphenophyllum oblongifolium* Germar is distinguished by the edges of the leaves being convex outwards. Although it has been recorded, it is doubtful whether this species occurs in Britain. The specimens figured on Plate X, *h*, *i* resemble *S. fasciculatum* Lesqx. and *S. longifolium* Germar respectively, but I believe them to be distinct from those species.

CHAPTER IV

EQUISETALES

The Equisetales* were among the commonest and most widely distributed groups of Carboniferous plants. While they were mostly trees, a few were herbaceous, and some of the latter (provisionally included in *Equisetites* Sternberg) had leaves which took the form of toothed sheaths and cones which (as in living "horsetails" or "scouring rushes") contained fertile bracts only. The cones were so similar superficially to those of the recent *Equisetum* as to suggest a near relationship. It is doubtful, however, whether the Palæozoic impressions designated *Equisetites* belong to the same group as the Mesozoic *Equisetites* (plants much larger than but similar in all essentials to living horsetails and clearly closely related to them). The commoner tree-forms of the Palæozoic Equisetales (*Calamites*—with free leaves and cones which had alternate fertile and sterile whorls of bracts) persisted until the Jurassic; they reached a height of 50 feet or more, the trunk attaining a diameter of several feet. From a thick creeping or underground stem (with its whorls of roots) arose branches which themselves gave rise to whorl after whorl of successively smaller branches borne at certain of the nodes. As the plant grew the older branches were shed, and their position may be detected by the branch-scars which occur on some of the casts of the stem and pith-cavities. The familiar whorls of leaves were borne at the nodes on the younger branches. *Calamites* lived in swamps, and the possession of creeping and underground stems tended to produce a dense, jungle-like growth. Some "paper coals" are found to consist largely of the cuticles of these plants, while it is probable that many (but by no means all) of the wedges of fusain ("mineral charcoal" or "mother of coal") which are visible on a broken

---

* The Equistales include (1) *Asterocalamites* (= *Archæocalamites*), impressions from the Lower Carboniferous in which the ribs on the internodes did not alternate and with forked leaves. (2) *Pothocites*, casts of large cones bearing leaves like those of *Asterocalamites* (Lower Carboniferous). (3) *Calamites*, chiefly in the Coal Measures. Structurally preserved stems are divided into *Arthropitys*, *Arthrodendron*, and *Calamodendron*. (4) Mesozoic forms (incrustations): (a) *Equisetites*, chiefly Triassic, with sheathing leaves and other resemblances to the recent *Equisetum*. (b) *Schizoneura*, a Triassic form in which the leaf-sheath splits almost to the base, forming segments. (c) *Neocalamites* (Triassic) in which each vascular bundle traversed at least two internodes and the leaves were separate (like those of *Asterophyllites*). (d) *Phyllotheca* (from Permian to lower Jurassic), with leaves fused and sheathing at base but with long spreading linear segments and cones in which fertile and sterile whorls alternated. (5) *Equisetum*, the living "horsetails."

surface of humic (so-called bituminous) coals represent the wood of detached nodes of Calamitean stems.

When dealing with impressions, *Calamites* Suckow usually refers to casts in shale or sandstone of the pith-cavities of stems and branches. Pith-casts of branches can sometimes be recognised by the fact that they taper and curve towards the point of attachment to the stem. Casts of large stems may measure a foot or so in diameter, and some idea can be formed of the size these plants attained when it is remembered that a broad cylinder of secondary wood surrounded the pith and that this was in turn enclosed by a thick cortex. Pith-casts of *Calamites* bear longitudinal ribs and distinct joints (nodes) which are sometimes constricted. In many cases they have lost their cylindrical form owing to being crushed in fossilisation, and early observers compared them with iris leaves, reeds, and pieces of sugar-cane. At a later date, when their stem-nature was recognised, they were supposed to represent the outer surface of the original stem. Actually, casts of the outer surface of Calamitean stems are rare. Although the surface of the young stem was sometimes longitudinally ribbed (as in the adult stem of the recent *Equisetum*), that of the older stems was usually smooth and only occasionally slightly ribbed. As casts and impressions of the outer surface cannot always be correlated with their corresponding pith-casts, etc., the late Dr. Arber proposed two new genera to receive them—*Calamophloios* (in which the internodes were smooth, or, if striated, the striæ were not reticulate) and *Dictyocalamites* (with reticulate striations on the internodes). Besides nodes, internodes, and branch-scars, these fossils may show leaf-scars, and root-scars are often borne on the nodes (and sometimes on the internodes).

As in other Coal Measure stems (e.g. *Sigillaria* and *Lepidodendron*), we may find Calamitean stems which show markings due to tissues within the cortex or to the outer surface of the woody cylinder; the former show neither nodes nor ribs, while the latter may be ribbed and simulate pith-casts, but infranodal canals are absent. Circular fossils are also occasionally found representing transverse impressions of the nodes. These specimens are of little botanical or geological value.

To return to the common pith-casts: the pith of the stem of *Calamites* broke down at an early stage of development, at first leaving diaphragms of tissue at the nodes, but these later being reduced to mere rings. The fossils were formed by sediment which filled the pith-cavity and show the markings of the inner surface of the woody cylinder:—

(*a*) Nodes, which may be constricted, and internodes.

(*b*) Longitudinal furrows on the internodes, due to wedges of wood projecting into the pith-cavity.

(*c*) Raised ribs between the furrows marking the position of the soft medullary rays.

(*d*) Well preserved specimens bear, on each ridge just below the node, a small tubercle indicating the position of a canal of soft tissue which passed through the medullary ray and opened into the pith—the "infranodal canals" of Williamson.

(*e*) Above some of the nodes are occasionally found one or more fairly large, usually circular or oval, scars, representing the depressions left by branches which had been shed.

Weiss divided the genus *Calamites* into three sub-genera (*Calamitina*, *Eucalamites*, and *Stylocalamites*), according to the branching and other features, but the groups have little value. In pith-casts of *Calamites* the ribs on successive internodes usually alternate, but in the Lower Carboniferous genus *Asterocalamites* Schimper they pass straight through the nodes.*

Calamites cisti Brongt. (Plates XI, *a*; XXXVII, *e*) has internodes 2–16 cm. long by 3–10 cm. broad, and is distinguished from *C. cruciatus* by the nodes not being constricted. The ribs gradually taper to a rather blunt point. They are longitudinally striated, while the furrows are double-lined (compare *C. carinatus*, Plates XI, *b*; XXIV, *d*). In *C. cisti* the upper tubercles are elliptical, but in *C. carinatus*, when seen (which is rare), they are oval. The nodes of *C. carinatus* are slightly constricted and the angle at the top of the ribs rounded or obtuse. A typical feature of *C. carinatus* is the branch scars (generally absent from *C. cisti*). They have a large central opening and the ribs bend towards each other at the margin.

Calamites sachsei Stur (*pars*) (Plates XI, *c*; XXXVIII, *g*) stands nearest to *C. gœpperti* Ett. (Plates XI, *d*; XXIV, *f*). In both species the internodes are nearly always broader than long, but those of *C. sachsei* are much shorter than those of *C. gœpperti*. The branch-scars of *C. sachsei* are practically circular, though tending to be deformed by mutual pressure; those of *C. gœpperti* are almost square. *C. sachsei* has whorls of branch-scars separated by intervals of three to ten branchless nodes. In *C. gœpperti*, on the other hand, the arrangement of the branch-scars was irregular, there being no definite succession of branched and non-branched nodes.

Calamites schützeiformis Kidston and Jongmans (Plate XXIV, *c*) is a very variable species, three forms having been recognised. In forma *typicus* the internodes are from 0·75 to 9·0 cm. long, the shortest occurring just above the branch-whorls and the longest just below. The branch-whorls are separated by four to nine internodes, and the ribs are prominent. In forma *intermedius* the internodes are from 0·4 to 1·7 cm. long, the two longest occurring above and below the branch-whorls, while in forma *waldenburgensis* (the *C. approximatus* Brongt. (*pars*), with internodes from 0·3 to 1·5 cm. long, and much constricted at the nodes, the longest occur just below the branch-whorl. In this form the whorls of branch-scars are separated by five to eighteen or more internodes, and the ribs are very prominent.

Calamites suckowi Brongt. (Plates XI, *e*; XXIV, *a*) is the commonest species of the genus and occurs at all levels in the Coal Measures. The internodes are from 3 to 15 cm. long by 3 to 20 cm. broad, and the nodes

* In *Sphenophyllum*, where the ribs on the stems pass straight through the nodes, we are dealing with the outer surface of the pithless stem.

are not constricted. The ribs are always straight (contrast *C. undulatus*). Characteristic features are the bluntly rounded angle formed at the top of the ribs and the longitudinal striations borne on the ribs. The upper tubercles are oval or circular. Lower tubercles are usually absent, as are branch-scars.

Calamites undulatus Sternb. (Plates XI, *f*; XXIV, *b*) is a common species, especially in the Yorkian and Lanarkian Series. Though the ribs may be straight, they are often slightly flexuous. The whorls of branch-scars are periodically distributed, being separated by a number of nodes from which branches were absent. The species is distinguished by (1) the sharp (almost right) angles at the top of the ribs, (2) the cross-hatching of the upper surface of the ribs, (3) the small upper tubercles (not more than 1 mm. across), and (4) the fact that lower (dot-like) tubercles are not always present. The leafy branches corresponding to *C. undulatus* are known as *Asterophyllites charæformis*.

The genus *Annularia* Sternberg includes certain branches bearing whorls of leaves, many of which belonged to *Calamites*. The leaves may be linear, lanceolate, or spathulate, but are always broader than in *Asterophyllites*. The members of a given whorl were often of unequal length. Whorls of *Annularia* leaves were compared by early writers with asters and other recent flowers; they were spread out in one plane and united at the base to form a small collar round the stem (though this fusion is not always observable in specimens). *Asterophyllites* Brongniart (= *Calamocladus* Schimper) refers to slender branchlets of *Calamites* which were given off in opposite pairs at each node; they bore whorls of four to forty linear leaves which were neither spread out in one plane nor united at the base. In both of these genera the leaves contained a single vein.

Annularia microphylla Sauveur (Plates X, *j*; XXV, *a*) is very similar to *A. galioides* (L. and H.) (Plate X, *k*), the lanceolate leaves being up to 5 or 6 mm. long and 1 mm. broad, usually in whorls of about a dozen. The leaves of *A. microphylla*, however, are bent and sickle-shaped, with the margins rolled inwards; those of *A. galioides* are straight and flat. The leaves of *A. microphylla* are narrower in proportion to their length than those of *A. galioides*, and the apex tapers much more gradually. A further distinction is that the vein in *A. microphylla* is situated in a distinct furrow, which is absent from *A. galioides*.

Annularia radiata Brongt. (Plates X, *m*; XXV, *b*) is the foliage of *Calamites carinatus*. The leaves are linear-lanceolate and taper to a very sharp point. The bases of the leaves in the same whorl do not touch, and the leaves of a whorl are usually of the same length (contrast *A. stellata*). Individual leaves are 5–20 mm. long and 0·5–2 mm. broad, and successive whorls often overlap each other.

Annularia stellata (Schloth.) (Plates X, *l*; XXV, *h*) has leaves which are 1–5 or more cm. long and 1–3 mm. broad, sixteen to thirty-two in a whorl. The widest part occurs beyond the middle, and the leaf tapers (more quickly than in *A. radiata*) to a blunt point. The bases of the leaves touch at the edges, and there is generally a little inequality in length. The successive whorls touch or overlap each other only slightly.

Annularia sphenophylloides (Zenker) (Plates X, *n*; XXV, *f*) has spoon-shaped leaves which are narrow at the base, broaden towards the apex, and end in a more or less sharp point. As in *A. stellata*, there is some inequality in the members composing a given whorl, so that the whorls tend to be elliptical. The successive whorls usually touch each other. Individual leaves are 3–10 mm. long and 1–3 mm. broad at the widest point.

The various species of *Asterophyllites* are difficult to separate in the barren condition, *A. grandis*, for example, appearing to show transitions not only to *A. charæformis*, but also to *A. equisetiformis*. The cones of these "species" are, however, distinct, and it is very probable that each type of leaf bore more than one species of fructification.

A. equisetiformis (Schloth.) (Plates X, *o*; XXV, *c*), fairly common on most Coal Measure horizons, has whorls of spreading needle-shaped leaves which are sharply pointed. They are smaller than in *A. longifolius* (Sternb.) (Plate X, *r*), but larger than in *A. charæformis* (Sternb.) (Plates X, *p*; XXV, *e*) and *A. grandis* (Sternb.) (Plate X, *q*).

The fructifications of these plants consisted of narrow cones terminating the slender branches. Average specimens measure 5–8 cm. in length by 0·5–1 cm. across, but some attained 30 cm. in length and 3 cm. or so across. They are named, according to their structure, *Calamostachys* Schimper, *Palæostachya* Weiss, *Volkmannia* Sternberg, and *Macrostachya* Schimper. Some species were homosporous (like the modern *Equisetum*), others hetero-sporous. The cones were shed from the plants when ripe and fertilisation occurred on the damp ground. In *Calamostachys* the narrow cones consist of alternate whorls of fertile and sterile bracts, the former taking the form of sporangiophores attached at right-angles to the cone-axis, midway between the sterile whorls. They bear four sporangia attached to a peltate expansion. *Stachannularia* Weiss (Plate XXV, *g*) is similar, but the sporangiophores are thorn-like structures bearing on their upper side a blade-like expansion. *Calamostachys* cones have been found connected with branches bearing leaves of *Annularia sphenophylloides* and *A. stellata*, as well as with the *Astero-phyllites* type of foliage. In *Palæostachya* (Plate XXV, *i, j*) the sporangiophores are attached in or just above the axil of the sterile bracts. The cones of *P. gracillima* were up to 6 cm. long and appear to have been sessile. Poorly preserved examples of *Palæostachya* cannot be distinguished from *Cala-mostachys*. *Macrostachya* (Plate XXV, *d*) is larger than *Calamostachys* or *Palæostachya*, measuring up to 20 cm. in length and 3·2 cm. across, and the imbricating whorls of bracts are more closely placed. Each whorl consists of about twenty bracts united except at the extremity, where they divide to form short pointed teeth. *Volkmannia*, as applied to impressions, includes cones having the general appearance of *Calamostachys* and *Palæostachya*, but in which the disposition of the fertile bracts is unknown.

The roots of the Palæozoic Equisetales (and of many other contemporaneous plants) show no distinguishing features and are difficult to classify. They are grouped together under the designation *Pinnularia* Lindley and Hutton (Plate **XXXV**, *c*). The great similarity in the form and structure of the roots of vascular plants, both fossil and recent, is clearly due to the uniform conditions of growth underground.

CHAPTER V

CORDAITALES AND CONIFERALES

The Cordaitales* belonged to the Gymnosperms, and were both very common and very widely distributed in Coal Measure times. They became extinct in the Permian. Some French coal seams are almost entirely composed of the leaves of these plants.

Cordaites were trees which attained and even exceeded 100 feet in height. The trunk was comparatively slender (up to about 2 feet in diameter), and was unbranched except at the crown, which consisted of many scattered branches. The branches bore numerous spirally arranged sessile leaves. In general appearance the tree would resemble the recent Australian Kauri Pine (*Agathis robusta*).

Cordaites Unger, as applied to incrustations, includes various types of leaves with parallel veins which were borne by stems structurally referred to the fairly common *Mesoxylon* Scott and the rarer *Cordaites* (*Cordaioxylon* Schenk) and *Poroxylon* Renault, as well as possibly to other stem types as yet uncorrelated with them. The leaves, which were often of large dimensions (2 to 3 feet in length) and sword-like, persisted for some years. The narrower leaves were grass-like. They were attached directly to the stem, and, on falling from the tree, left a transversely oval scar on the stem which remained for some time and showed a curved row of dot-like scars indicating the points at which the veins passed into the leaf. Similar markings occur on the bases of the leaves. Although the leaves grouped under *Cordaites* are common Coal Measure fossils, stems (*Cordaicladus*) are rare, and this and other features suggest that the plants grew not in the Coal Measure swamps themselves, but on the gentle slopes surrounding the marshy ground.

Grand 'Eury based three sub-genera on the shape and size of the leaf.

* The Cordaitales are provisionally divided into: (1) the Poroxyleæ (*Poroxylon*—petrified stems and leaves from the Permo-Carboniferous of France, the corresponding seeds appearing to have been of the *Rhabdocarpus* type). (2) The Pityeæ (petrified stems—*Pitys* from the Lower Carboniferous of Scotland, *Archæopitys* from the Lower Carboniferous of Kentucky, and *Callixylon* from the Upper Devonian of South Russia). (3) The Cordaiteæ (Upper Carboniferous and Permian petrified stems—*Cordaites*, stems without centripetal wood; *Mesoxylon*, stems with centripetal wood; *Mesoxylopsis*, differing from *Mesoxylon* (and *Cordaites*) in having a single leaf-trace leaving the stele; *Parapitys; Cænoxylon; Mesopitys; Metacordaites*). Petrified fructifications of the Cordaiteæ are known, but as yet cannot be assigned to particular members of the family. These are placed in *Cordaianthus*, which probably also includes the fructification of *Mesoxylon*, etc.

In *Eucordaites* the leaf was spathulate and large (up to 2 or 3 feet in length and several inches in breadth), while the apex was rounded. *Dorycordaites* includes fairly large lanceolate leaves with pointed apices. *Poacordaites* refers to small narrow grass-like leaves with obtuse apices.

Cordaites angulosostriatus Grand 'Eury (Plate **XXXIV**, *a*) is the only common *Cordaites* leaf in the Radstockian; it is unknown from the Yorkian or Lanarkian Series. The leaves are large and strap-shaped, with parallel "veins." In all species of *Cordaites* there are a number of veins and ribs which run parallel to the margin of the leaf and seldom fork. As it is impossible in impressions to distinguish between true veins and lines merely representing longitudinal strands of sclerenchyma, the distinctions between "species," so far as they are based on the "veins," are unsatisfactory. Moreover, owing to decay, the finer lines may have disappeared from the impression, a feature which seems to apply especially to *C. borassifolius* (Plates XI, *h*; XXXIV, *d*).

The leaves of *C. borassifolius* (Sternb.) are lanceolate, with an obtuse apex. They measure 12–25 mm. at the base and 3–10 cm. in the middle, and attain a length of 60 cm. The "veins" are alternately thick and thin, and are farther apart than in *C. principalis* (Plates XI, *i*; XXXIV, *c*). In the last-named species the leaves are broadly lanceolate, with an apex which is more obtuse than in *C. borassifolius*, and which therefore tends to split; they are up to 50 cm. in length and measure 3–6 cm. in the middle. One to five fine lines occur between each pair of stronger "veins" (eight to ten per millimetre).

Dorycordaites palmæformis (Goeppert) (Plates XI, *g*; XXXIV, *f*) includes linear-lanceolate leaves with typically acute apices. The base measures up to 5 cm. and the middle up to 1 cm. across, while the leaf may reach 60 cm. in length. The "veins" are of equal strength and very fine, eight to twelve occurring in each millimetre.

Poacordaites microstachys (Gold.) (Plate **XXXIV**, *b*) represents linear leaves with obtuse apices, not more than 1 cm. wide and up to 30 cm. long. The "veins" are either equal or with one or two alternating striæ, very closely placed.

Artisia Sternberg (= *Sternbergia* Artis) represents the pith-casts of some of the Cordaitales (though similar casts may be formed in other plants). The young stems of *Mesoxylon* and *Cordaites* had a relatively large and solid pith which did not keep pace in growth with the elongation of the stem. This resulted in a rupture of the pith at intervals, leaving occasional diaphragms of tissue. During continued growth most of the diaphragms broke down, and a more or less continuous pith-cavity was formed with only remnants of the diaphragms surrounding it. (A similar type of pith occurs in certain recent plants, e.g. the walnut.) *Artisia* is a cylindrical cast up to 3 or 4 inches in diameter and sometimes of considerable length. Transverse constrictions, representing the diaphragms of pith, occur at varying intervals. The size and markings on the casts have no specific value, nor has *Artisia* any stratigraphical value.

The reproductive organs corresponding to the structure-stems *Mesoxylon* and *Poroxylon* are as yet unknown, though they are probably included among those referred to the nearly related *Cordaites* of structure. The relatively short staminate (microspore- or pollen-bearing) catkins are known as *Cordaianthus* Grand 'Eury (previously *Antholithus* Brongniart, a term, however, which was somewhat loosely used), while the larger ovulate (seed-bearing) catkins were placed in the genus *Cordaicarpus* Geinitz. The last-named genus now refers to some of the flat, often slightly winged seeds which were borne on the catkins, though not all seeds of this type belonged to the Cordaitales. (At least one Pteridosperm—*Dicksonites pluckeneti*—bore *Samaropsis* seeds: there is no sharp dividing line between *Cordaicarpus* and *Samaropsis*.) As they are similar in outward appearance, many authors place both the "male" and the "female" catkins in *Cordaianthus*.

The figure of *Cordaianthus volkmanni* (Ett.) (Plate **XXXIV**, *e*) shows an ovulate shoot with seeds. The bracts in the angles of which the seeds are borne are characteristically large. *C. pitcairniæ* (L. and H.) (Plate **XXXIV**, *g*) is an ovulate shoot bearing seeds known as *Samaropsis acuta* (L. and H.).

Walchia Sternberg, which occurs very rarely in the Coal Measures, represents the earliest known genus of the Coniferales,[*] and is probably closely related to the Araucarineæ. It includes leafy branches having a general resemblance to the Norfolk Island Pine (*Araucaria excelsa*), and sometimes ending in cones which seldom, however, contain preserved seeds. The ultimate branches are pinnately arranged on the older stems and bear closely placed spirals of overlapping leaves. Fragmentary specimens, in which the pinnate branching cannot be recognised, might be mistaken for leafy branches of *Lepidodendron*.

W. imbricata Schimper (Plate **XXXVI**, *k*) is very similar to the leafy branches of *Araucaria rulei*, though smaller. It chiefly occurs in the Permian and the Stephanian of the Continent, but one or two examples have been recorded from the Radstockian and Staffordian Series of Britain. The fairly broad and short leaves are markedly incurved and overlapping. *Walchia piniformis* (Schloth.) (Plate **XXXVI**, *l*) has a similar distribution and is commoner. The pinnately arranged lateral branches stand obliquely to the older stems. The decurrent leaves are fairly long, narrow, and sickle-shaped. *W. hypnoides* (Brongt.) is probably only a small form of *W. piniformis*.

---

[*] The Coniferales comprise :—
  (1) Taxaceæ (no true cones, ovules single, freely exposed and with a fleshy collar).
    (*a*) Taxineæ, including *Taxus* (Yew).
    (*b*) Podocarpæ—*Podocarpus*, etc.
  (2) Pinacæ (with true cones, ovules protected by scales, lacking a collar, seeds dry).
    (*a*) Araucarineæ (*Araucaria, Agathis*).
    (*b*) Abietineæ (*Pinus, Picea, Larix, Abies, Cedrus*).
    (*c*) Taxodineæ (*Taxodium, Sequoia, Sciadopitys, Cryptomeria*).
    (*d*) Cupressineæ (*Cupressus, Thuja, Juniperus*).

CHAPTER VI

FILICALES AND PTERIDOSPERMEÆ

It has already been observed that the fern-like leaves* of the Coal Measures were originally thought to have belonged entirely to ferns, but that many belonged to Pteridosperms, plants with foliage like that of ferns but bearing seeds like those of the Cycads (and hence called by American authors the Cycadofilices). It is probable that the Pteridosperms and the Cycads arose from a common (unknown) ancestor. The Pteridosperms became extinct in the Permian. The ferns,† on the other hand, have persisted from the Palæozoic to the present day, though no Carboniferous species is known to have passed beyond the Permian and the family at present predominant (the Polypodiaceæ—e.g. Bracken, Male Fern, Spleenworts, and Hart's-tongue Fern) cannot be traced back with certainty beyond the Jurassic.

Both ferns and Pteridosperms are characterised by large leaves (contrast *Sphenophyllum* and *Calamites*) and by the fact that the fructifications were borne on the leaves (not aggregated in cones as in *Lepidodendron*, *Sphenophyllum*, *Calamites*, etc., or in unisexual catkins as in the Cordaitales). The plants included herbaceous forms, some having the general habit of the modern Spleenwort (*Asplenium*). Others were slender-stemmed scramblers, relying for support on the surrounding vegetation. *Lyginopteris* (= *Lyginodendron*) was of this type, and its stems and leaves were covered with spines, a feature common in scramblers. Others, again, and these were especially frequent towards the end of Coal Measure times, had the habit of tree-ferns, with stems 2 or more feet in diameter and up to 70 feet in height; they were clothed with a thick felt of innumerable descending roots and bore a large crown of massive spreading fronds. The considerable development of air spaces in many of the roots suggests that some of these tree-ferns grew

---

* Many of the impressions of fern and fern-like leaves of the Coal Measures show considerable resemblance to the leaves of living ferns, though there can be no near relationship between them. *Sphenopteris dilatata*, for example, has a resemblance to the Wall Rue (*Asplenium ruta-muraria*), *Alethopteris serli* to the Common Polypody (*Polypodium vulgare*), *Alethopteris lonchitica* to the Hard Fern (*Blechnum boreale*) and species of *Neuropteris* to the Royal Fern (*Osmunda regalis*). *Sphenopteris dilatata* may have been the foliage of a fern, but, if so, the fructification would be of a primitive type and very different from that of the advanced *Asplenium*. On the other hand, *Alethopteris serli*, *A. lonchitica*, and *Neuropteris* were the leaves of Pteridosperms.

† A detailed account of the ferns, both fossil and recent, will be found in Professor F. O. Bower's *The Ferns* (*Filicales*), vols. i–iii, 1923–8, Cambridge Botanical Handbooks.

in swampy ground. Others no doubt inhabited the gentle slopes and higher ground surrounding the swamps.

Some of the tree-ferns, the *Cyatheites-Pecopterids*, bore highly compound pecopteroid leaves (now placed in *Acitheca*, *Scolecopteris*, *Asterotheca*, and *Ptychocarpus*) similar in shape to those of the recent (tropical) *Cyathea.** Stems of the *Cyatheites-Pecopterids* are preserved both as petrifactions (*Psaronius* Unger) and as incrustations (*Caulopteris* L. and H., *Megaphyton* Artis, and *Ptychopteris* Corda). One member of the group (*Dicksonites pluckeneti*) has been found bearing seeds (as well as indications of microsporangia) and was clearly a Pteridosperm, and Dr. Kidston gradually came to suspect that the whole group was Pteridospermous, chiefly because the synangia resemble *Telangium*. Dr. Scott, however, basing his opinion on the undoubted fernlike structure of *Psaronius*, inclines to the original view that most of the *Cyatheites-Pecopterids* were Marattiaceous ferns.†

Some of the Pteridosperms which bore *Neuropteris* and *Alethopteris* foliage were also tree-ferns. The seeds of *Neuropteris obliqua* and *N. heterophylla* are placed in *Neuropterocarpus*, while the common *Trigonocarpus parkinsoni* was in all probability the seed of *Alethopteris lonchitica* (the stems of which, when preserved structurally, are known as *Medullosa anglica*).

The barren leaves of ferns and Pteridosperms, when preserved as impressions, are provisionally placed in various form genera based upon their shape, venation, etc., the chief Coal Measure genera being *Linopteris* Presl (= *Dictyopteris* Gutbier), *Lonchopteris* Brongniart, *Alethopteris* Sternberg, *Pecopteris* Brongniart, *Neuropteris* Brongniart, *Odontopteris* Brongniart, *Sphenopteris* Brongniart, and *Mariopteris* Zeiller. Their distinguishing features are given in the form of a key on page 49.

When leaves provisionally placed in the above form genera are found with sporangia attached, they are removed to genera based upon the type of fructification borne. In this way many leaves originally included in *Sphenopteris* are now placed in *Corynepteris*, *Oligocarpia*, *Renaultia*, and *Urnatopteris*, and many Radstockian pecopteroid fronds in *Asterotheca*, *Acitheca*, *Scolecopteris*, *Dactylotheca*, and *Dicksonites*. Only when seeds are found attached to the leaves can we be absolutely sure that we are dealing with a Pteridosperm and not a fern, though in many cases the indirect evidence is very strong.

Diplotmema Stur (as restricted by Zeiller) is mainly distinguished from *Sphenopteris* by the fact that the primary pinnæ fork into two equal branches;

---

* This is an external similarity only: the fructification of *Cyathea* shows a considerable advance on that of the *Cyatheites-Pecopterids*, and the two groups cannot have been closely related.

† The living Marattiaceæ are tropical ferns of large size with simple sori or sporangia. The stems are not clothed in a mass of rootlets as was the case in the *Cyatheites-Pecopterids*. If the *Cyatheites-Pecopterids* eventually prove to have been Pteridosperms, there would still have been two undoubted groups of ferns in the Palæozoic: the Cœnopterideæ, ranging from the Lower Carboniferous to the Permian, and the Permian Osmundaceæ, both groups being represented by petrifactions.

I. SECONDARY VEINS FORM A NETWORK:

    (i) *Linopteris**—pinnules attached by a single point, base more or less cordate; shape of pinnules as in *Neuropteris*.

    (ii) *Lonchopteris**—pinnules attached by whole breadth of base, often decurrent; shape of pinnules as in *Alethopteris*.

II. SECONDARY VEINS FORKED OR SIMPLE, NOT FORMING A NETWORK:

    (*a*) Pinnules with a distinct midrib which continues to apex; attached by whole breadth of base, often decurrent:

        (i) *Alethopteris**—pinnules long and linear, secondary veins many, almost at right-angles to midrib.

        (ii) *Pecopteris*†‡—pinnules short, margins often nearly parallel, secondary veins comparatively few, almost at right-angles to midrib, pinnules not contracted at base.

    (*b*) Pinnules with an indistinct midrib which does not continue to apex; pinnules oval or tongue-shaped, entire, rarely lobed:

        (i) *Neuropteris**—pinnules attached by a single point to rachis, base more or less cordate; one vein (the midrib) enters pinnule from rachis, then forks several times, producing secondary veins which arch.

        (ii) *Odontopteris**—pinnules attached by whole breadth of base, often decurrent; several veins enter pinnule from rachis, then fork several times, producing secondary veins which arch.

    (*c*) Pinnules contracted at base, often lobed or toothed:

        (i) *Sphenopteris*†—pinnules small and often wedge-shaped at base; veins radiate in a fan-like manner from base of pinnule.

        (ii) *Mariopteris**—pinnules large and leathery; rachis of primary pinna forks twice.

---

* Most or all the leaves included in these genera belonged to Pteridosperms, though *attached* seeds have yet to be found in many instances.

† Many of these leaves belonged to Pteridosperms, but some were almost certainly the foliage of ferns.

‡ Brongniart's form genus *Pecopteris* has recently been divided into Radstockian forms (*Asterotheca*, etc., and *Eupecopteris*) and Yorkian forms. See page 55.

it probably represents the foliage of Pteridosperms. *Cyclopteris* Brongniart refers to impressions of large or small rounded leaves which occurred directly on the main rachis of various species of *Neuropteris, Odontopteris, Linopteris, Margaritopteris,* and *Alethopteris.* In these appendages the veins radiate out from the base of the leaf. Somewhat similar organs which occurred on certain fronds of *Pecopteris* and *Sphenopteris* are pinnate or pinnatafid and are placed in *Aphlebia* Presl (= *Rhacophyllum* Schimper). *Cyclopteris* and *Aphlebia* are usually found isolated, and have been interpreted as separate ferns, epiphytic ferns, or even as algæ. They probably protected the young buds from desiccation. *Spiropteris* Schimper includes young unopened leaves of ferns and Pteridosperms.

Caulopteris refers to casts of the stems of the *Cyatheites-Pecopterids* with circular or oval leaf-scars which are spirally arranged. Near the upper end of the leaf-scar is the U-shaped scar of the vascular bundle. In *Megaphyton* the larger oval scars occur in two opposite rows, each scar alternating with one on the opposite side of the stem. Here the scar of the vascular bundle forms a closed ring. In *Ptychopteris* are placed decorticated examples of these stems.

GROUP I. SPHENOPTERIDEÆ*

Sphenopteris schatzlarensis (Stur) (Plates **XII**, *a*; **XXV**, *l*) stands nearest to *Boweria*† *schatzlarensis* Kidston (Plate **XII**, *b*), the two forms being at one time united. The larger ultimate pinnæ measure about 1 cm. long by 4 mm. wide (in *B. schatzlarensis* they attain 3·5 cm. in length). The pinnules are also smaller than in *B. schatzlarensis,* as are the two or three pairs of segments which they bear, while the sides of the segments are straighter. In *S. schatzlarensis* the segments usually end in sharp points. In *B. schatzlarensis* the points are blunt. Altogether, *S. schatzlarensis* is a more slender and lax-growing plant.

Sphenopteris macilenta L. and H. (Plates **XII**, *c*; **XXXII**, *f*) is a very distinctive species. The pinnules are alternate and large, and are divided (according to their position on the frond) into two to five prominent, bluntly rounded lobes.

Sphenopteris trifoliolata (Artis) (Plates **XII**, *d*; **XXXII**, *g*) was a very large frond, and great variations occurred in the shape and division of the pinnules according to their position. The pinnules are often divided into three rounded lobes, and the species is distinguished from *S. striata* Gothan (Plate **XXXII**, *h*) (the pinnules of which are also sometimes divided into three rounded lobes) by the smaller and almost always separated pinnules, the whole plant having a laxer type of growth. The pinnules in *S. trifoliolata* are often convex and the veins rarely seen. In *S. striata* the outer surface of the pinnule is striated.

Sphenopteris laurenti Andrae (Plates **XII**, *f*; **XXXII**, *d*) is closely allied

---

* Like some of the genera they contain, these groups are for descriptive convenience only. The plants included in them are not necessarily related.

† *Boweria* Kidston has free marginal oval sporangia, each with an annulus composed of two rows of cells.

to *Renaultia** *rotundifolia* (Andrae) (Plates XII, *g*; XXXIII, *b*). While in *S. laurenti* the ultimate pinnæ are lanceolate, in *R. rotundifolia* they are shorter and more triangular. The pinnules of the former are roughly triangular and smaller and more distant than in *R. rotundifolia*, where they are oblong-lanceolate. *S. laurenti* had a laxer type of growth. The fine teeth borne on the lobes of the pinnules of *S. laurenti* are also distinctive. Both these species resemble *S. stipulata* (Gutbier) (Plate XIII, *a*), but here the pinnæ are more triangular than in *R. rotundifolia*, while the oblong pinnules are often less segmented on the lower than on the upper margin.

Sphenopteris neuropteroides (Boulay) (Plates XII, *h*; XXXII, *e*) has pinnules which take the form of a square with rounded angles; the upper pinnules are entire, the lower with two more or less distinct lobes. There is some similarity to *S. striata* (Plates XII, *e*; XXXII, *h*), but the square pinnules are distinctive. These are attached by a broad base, whereas in *S. striata* there is a distinct stalk. The surface of typical pinnules of *S. striata* bears fine striations.

Sphenopteris spiniformis Kidston (Plates XII, *i*; XXXI, *f*) has been confused with *S. artemisæfolioides* Crépin (of which there are no satisfactory records from this country). In the former the apex of the pinnæ and of the pinnule segments end in sharp, spine-like points, while in the latter they are rounded. The pinnules of *S. spiniformis* were up to 2 or more cm. in length and 1·5 cm. in breadth, directed forwards and attached by a broad stalk.

Sphenopteris alata Brongt. (Plates XII, *j*; XXXII, *a*), a Radstockian plant, has some similarity to *Diplotmema furcatum* (Brongt.) (Plates XII, *k*; XXX, *h*), a Yorkian form. In both species the rachis is winged, but this feature is more marked in the former. Both are also characterised by the segmentation of the pinnules, but in *S. alata* the pinnules and their segments are more closely placed and the segments less deeply cleft. While blunt points terminate the segments of *S. alata*, those of *D. furcatum* are sharp. The latter species has more resemblance to *S. spinosa* Goeppert, but the segments are longer and narrower and less close in *D. furcatum*, giving a laxer appearance, and, though the segments end in sharp points, they are not spine-like, as on some segments of *S. spinosa*.

Sphenopteris dilatata L. and H. (Plates XII, *l*; XXXIII, *a*) has been united to *S. trifoliolata* (Plates XII, *d*; XXXII, *g*). In both plants the pinnules are convex and distant, and the veins indistinct. The pinnules of *S. dilatata* are either simple or with one or two clefts midway to the base; those of *S. trifoliolata* are often three-lobed. In *S. dilatata* the upper margin of the pinnule suddenly bends down. Finally, *S. dilatata* is a rather larger and more open type of frond than *S. trifoliolata*.

Sphenopteris sauveuri Crépin (Plates XII, *m*; XXXIII, *h*), though not common, is a very distinctive species. Compared with *S. trifoliolata* (Artis) and *S. striata* Gothan, the pinnules are flat and are directed forwards towards the apex of the pinna, while the 2–6 lobes are more wedge-shaped and less rounded.

Oligocarpia† *gutbieri* Goeppert (Plates XII, *n*, XXXII *i*, a barren

---

* *Renaultia* Zeiller has free ovoid sporangia situated either singly or in groups of 2–5 towards the margin of the pinnules. There is no annulus.

† *Oligocarpia* Goeppert has circular synangia consisting of 3–5 (occasionally 6) pear-shaped sporangia. The annulus consists of two rows of cells. The synangia occur singly on the lateral veins.

specimen; XXXIV *i*, a fertile specimen): the pinnules are free and oval, with a wide attachment to the rachis, a blunt apex, blunt basal lobes, and sometimes two other slight lobes above them. In some pinnules, however, the lobes are reduced to a sinuous outline. The midrib gives rise to forking veinlets in the larger and to simple veinlets in the smaller pinnules. The synangia (groups of coherent sporangia) are circular, consisting of three to five pear-shaped sporangia, each about 0·5 mm. long.

Urnatopteris* *tenella* (Brongt.) (Plates XII, *o*; XXXV, *e*) is most like the much rarer and more robust *U. herbacea* (Boulay). The pinnules are directed forwards, divided into three to six bluntly pointed linear lobes. In *U. tenella* the pinnæ tend to be rhomboidal, while in *U. herbacea* they are lanceolate. Again, in *U. tenella* the pinnules are more deeply segmented.

Senftenbergia† *ophiodermatica* Goeppert, a Yorkian plant, consists of a large frond with oblong pinnules 2–3 mm. long by 1·25–1·5 mm. broad, arranged slightly obliquely, with entire margins, and ending in a blunt apex. The midrib is straight and strongly marked. On each side of the midrib are eight to ten oval sporangia covering the lower surface of the pinnule and placed close together. Sterile specimens are not known with certainty.

Eremopteris artemisæfolia (Sternb.) (Plates XII, *p*; XXXIII, *f*) could scarcely be confused with any other Coal Measure plant. The pinnules form an angle of about 45 degrees with the rachis. The shape of the pinnæ and the degree of division of the pinnules varies according to their position on the frond. The venation (shown in the enlargement figured) is distinctive; there is no midrib (contrast *Sphenopteris*). At the base of each pinnule are two or more veins which fork at an acute angle, the two forks keeping close together. Subsequent forks also keep close together for some distance before separating. The venation has some resemblance to that seen in the Lower Carboniferous genus *Sphenopteridium*, where, however, the pinnules are wedge-shaped.

Renaultia gracilis (Brongt.) (Plates XIII, *b*; XXXI, *h*; XXXIV, *h*) was once united to *Sphenopteris footneri* Marrat (Plate XIII, *c*), a very similar frond. In *R. gracilis* the adjacent pinnæ, which are broadly lanceolate, are distant, while in *S. footneri* they are triangular and either touch or overlap. The pinnules in *R. gracilis* are narrower than in *S. footneri* (about 2 mm. in the former and 3 mm. in the latter, where they are also more triangular and less deeply segmented). These features combine to give *R. gracilis* a much laxer appearance. The slightly undulating midrib gives off distinct lateral veinlets which are simple or forked (according to the size of the pinnule).

Corynepteris‡ *sternbergi* (Ett.) (Plate XXXII, *b*, *c*) is found in a fragmentary condition only. The linear secondary pinnæ are up to 5 cm. long and 1·5–4 mm. broad. The sessile and decurrent pinnules have a roughly square outline with three or four pointed teeth. This Yorkian species has

---

* In *Urnatopteris* Kidston the fertile leaves bear no foliage pinnules, the sporangia occurring alternately in two opposite rows on the rachis. They have no annulus.

† In *Senftenbergia* Corda the sterile and fertile pinnules are alike. The oval sporangia occur in a single row on each side of the midrib. The annulus is apical.

‡ In *Corynepteris* Baily the fertile and sterile pinnules may be alike, or the former may be somewhat reduced. The sporangia are large with a complete annulus passing up the sides and over the apex of the sporangium. Five or six sporangia are grouped to form a spherical sorus.

some resemblance to *Alloiopteris* serrula* (Lesqx.) (Plate XIII, *d*) and to *A. radstockensis* Kidston (Plate XIII, *e*), of which single examples only have been recorded, the former from the Staffordian and the latter from the Radstockian Series. It is distinguished from these by the squarer pinnules and sharper teeth, the central tooth projecting beyond the others.

Corynepteris coralloides (Gutbier) (Plates XII, *q*; XXXI, *g*) has alternate tertiary pinnæ bearing, almost at right-angles to the rachis, about seven pairs of very small pinnules. The latter do not exceed $1 \cdot 5$ mm. in length and are decurrent, with a slight basal contraction to form a broad stalk. They have two or three lobes, each of which may bear two or three teeth. The midrib is strongly marked, and gives off lateral veins forking in such a manner that one veinlet goes to each tooth.

Margaritopteris conwayi (L. and H.) (Plate XXXVII, *a*), originally figured as *Sphenopteris* (Lindley and Hutton, *Fossil Flora*, 1833–1835, vol. ii, plate 146), was later referred to *Odontopteris*, and is now placed in Gothan's genus *Margaritopteris*. The frond was large, coriaceous, and very thick, and the pinnules markedly convex. The pinnules were attached to the rachis by the whole breadth of their base and are characterised by the entire absence of a midrib.

Crossotheca† pinnatafida (Gutbier) (Plate XXXI, *e*) is a Radstockian plant of large dimensions, and the form of the pinnules varies greatly with their position on the frond. Some pinnules have a contracted base and simulate *Neuropteris*, but most are of the *Pecopteris* type. They may bear six or more rounded lobes. The central vein is stronger than in species of *Neuropteris*.

Radstockia‡ sphenopteroides (Kidston) (Plate XXXIII, *c*) had a rachis about 2 mm. broad bearing linear-lanceolate fertile pinnæ, no sterile leaves having been found. On each side of the rachis was a row of oblong sporangia united by their base in pairs.

Sphenopteris nummularia Gutbier (Plate XIII, *f*), a Yorkian and Lanarkian species, is more delicate and smaller than *S. striata* or *S. trifoliolata*; there are fewer pinnule lobes than in the former, while the shape of the pinnules distinguishes it from the latter. *S. schillingsi* Andrae (Plate XIII, *g*) has been rarely found in Britain. The pinnules are generally larger than in *S. striata* and the rachis is more slender. The distinct veins are much more spaced than in that species. *S. polyphylla* L. and H. (Plate XIII, *h*) has affinities with *S. trifoliolata* and *S. striata*, but the shape of the pinnule and the veins radiating from its base are distinctive. *S. pseudofurcata* Kidston (Plate XIII, *i*) differs from *Diplotmema furcatum* in having rounded apices and less spreading segments to its pinnules. In *S. alata* the segments are narrow and contain one vein only. *S. flabellifolia* Kidston (Plate XIII, *j*), a Lanarkian form, cannot be confused with any other species. *S. woodwardi* Kidston (Plate

---

* *Alloiopteris* Potonié probably represents sterile fronds of *Corynepteris*.

† *Crossotheca* Zeiller represents long narrow sporangia often, possibly always, bilocular, occurring on the lower side of the pinnules. The sterile leaves were of the types referred to *Sphenopteris*, *Rhodea*, and *Pecopteris*. It should be pointed out that both Professor Gothan and Mr. Hemingway consider that Dr. Kidston was in error in referring *Crossotheca* to *Sphenopteris hœninghausi* (the foliage of *Lyginopteris* which bore the seed known as *Lagenostoma*). Professor Gothan regards *Crossotheca* as a fern fructification : Mr. Hemingway suggests that it belonged to a Pteridosperm of the *Medullosa* type.

‡ *Radstockia* Kidston has large terminal sporangia, the upper surface of each bearing fine transverse bars which cover the whole sporangium.

XIII, *k*) has bifid lobes terminating in blunt points. *S. sewardi* Kidston (Plate XIII, *l*) bears small, sharply pointed teeth. The last two species are known from the Radstockian Series only.

Mariopteris nervosa (Brongt.) (Plates XIV, *s*; XXXIII, *d*) is a common and widespread plant, whereas *M. muricata* (Schloth.) (Plates XIV, *r*; XXXIII, *g*), with which it has been confused, is somewhat rare and restricted in distribution. The pinnules of *M. nervosa* are distinguished from those of *M. muricata* by their more triangular form, by the fact that their bases are nearly always united and seldom contracted, and by the general absence of lobing. *M. muricata* stands nearer to *M. acuta* (Brongt.) (Plates XV, *j*; XXXIX, *c*) and *M. nervosa* to *M. hirta* (Stur) (Plates XIV, *t*; XXXIX, *d*). In *M. muricata* the lobes point outwards, while in *M. acuta* they keep close to the margin of the pinnule. The pinnules of *M. nervosa* are narrower than those of *M. hirta* and taper from the base upwards; in *M. hirta* a distinct tapering is confined to the top half of the pinnule. The margins of the pinnules of *M. nervosa* are usually slightly concave; those of *M. hirta* are distinctly convex. In *M. sauveuri* (Brongt.) (Plate XXXIX, *e*) the pinnules are obtuse and their margins entire.

Mariopteris beneckei Huth (Plate XV, *k*) bears pinnules somewhat similar in shape and in the forward-directed blunt lobes to those of *M. latifolia* (Brongt.) (Plate XV, *l*), but in the latter they are typically closer.

GROUP II. PECOPTERIDEÆ

*Acitheca** polymorpha* (Brongt.) (Plates XIV, *a*; XXVI, *f*) is very similar to *Asterotheca*† *abbreviata* (Brongt.) (Plates XIV, *b*; XXVI, *d*) in the form of its sterile pinnules, and great variations occur in both species according to the position of the pinnules on the frond. In *polymorpha* the upper surface is smooth, while that of *A. abbreviata* is hairy (though this feature is not always preserved). In the former the midrib meets the rachis practically at a right-angle; in the latter the midrib is very distinctly decurrent. The lateral veins on the pinnules of *A. polymorpha* meet the margin almost at right-angles, while those of *A. abbreviata* take a more oblique course, arising from the midrib at an acute angle.

Asterotheca oreopteridia (Schloth.) (Plates XIV, *c*; XXVII, *g*) might also be mistaken for portions of *A. abbreviata*, but in the former only the fertile pinnules are hairy, while in the latter hairs are seen (where preserved) on both the fertile and the sterile leaflets. The median vein of *A. oreopteridia* is straight, and each lateral veinlet forks near the midrib (forming what Arber well described as a "tuning-fork" lateral nervation), while, on the larger pinnules, the upper division of the lower veinlets may fork again. In *A. abbreviata*, on the other hand, the median vein is clearly decurrent, and the lateral veins, which arise at an acute angle, divide once only.

Asterotheca daubreei (Zeiller) (Plates XIV, *d*; XXVII, *d*) can be distin-

---

* *Acitheca* Schimper bears sessile synangia composed usually of four sporangia, one row of synangia occurring on each side of the midrib. The sporangia had no annulus. In the similar *Scolecopteris* Zenker the synangia have a small stalk.

† *Asterotheca* Presl has ovoid exannulate sporangia four or five of which unite to form an almost sessile synangium.

guished from *A. oreopteridia* by the hairy covering (where preserved) on the sterile pinnules and by point-like marks which occur on the rachis. The veinlets are also more open immediately after the division.

Asterotheca crenulata (Brongt.) (Plates XIV, *e*; XXVII, *a*) has a very distinctive type of venation. The thick midrib gives rise to fine lateral veinlets which make with it an angle of about 45 degrees and generally divide once only into two straight arms. Crenulation of the margin of the pinnules is not necessarily present. On fertile specimens the synangia consist of star-like groups of four sporangia situated on the margins of the pinnules, above the ends of the veinlets.

Asterotheca cyathea (Schloth.) (Plates XIV, *f*; XXVII, *c*) has often been united to *A. arborescens* (Schloth.) (Plates XIV, *g*; XXVI, *a*). In the former the rachis is either smooth or with faint longitudinal striæ; in the latter it is smooth or with point-like marks. The pinnules of *A. cyathea* are longer in proportion to their width, and those occurring on the same pinna vary in length, a feature not seen in *A. arborescens*. The chief distinguishing feature consists in the lateral veins: in *A. cyathea* there is a mixture of forked and simple veinlets; in *A. arborescens* they are always simple.

*Dactylotheca** plumosa* (Artis) (Plates XIV, *h*; XXVI, *e*) had a very large frond and the characters of the pinnules varied considerably according to their position. Kidston united *Eupecopteris†* *dentata* (Brongt.) (Plate XXVI, *b*) with this species, but Mr. Hemingway regards them as distinct, and they are here provisionally kept apart. The venation is similar, but *E. dentata* appears to be more massive and more coriaceous, and has not been found in the fertile condition. The margins of the pinnules of *D. plumosa* often bear convex teeth, and in the larger leaflets the lower lateral veinlets generally fork once, the remainder being undivided, while in the smaller pinnules the veinlets are undivided.

Dicksonites‡ *pluckeneti* (Schloth.) (Plates XIV, *i*; XXVII, *b*) is a very distinctive Radstockian species. The pinnules are usually placed slightly obliquely on the rachis. Their shape (which is from oblong to oval) and the degree of segmentation vary with their position on the frond. The midrib is thick, undulating, and slightly decurrent, giving rise to lateral veinlets which fork two or three times.

Ptychocarpus§ *unitus* (Brongt.) (Plates XIV, *j*, *k*; XXVII, *i*) has Pecop-

---

* In *Dactylotheca* Zeiller the sterile pinnules are of the *Pecopteris* type and the fertile pinnules very little reduced. The latter bear exannulate, ovoid, free sporangia, which are longer than in *Renaultia*.

† *Eupecopteris* Gothan, as used by Kidston, includes the leaves of ferns and Pteridosperms which are at present known in the sterile condition only but which are similar in shape and venation to those fertile leaves formerly placed in *Pecopteris* Brongniart and now referred to *Asterotheca, Scolecopteris, Acitheca* and *Ptychocarpus*. Species in which the pinnules are Pecopteroid but not tongue-shaped, with varied venation (generally more lax than in *Eupecopteris*, and often Sphenopteroid) are retained under *Pecopteris*. *Eupecopteris* is typically Radstockian, *Pecopteris* (as thus limited) is Yorkian.

‡ *Dicksonites* Sterzel was a Pteridosperm, and both the seeds and the microsporangia, which were borne on different little-altered fronds, are known. The microsporangia are linear and arranged in star-like synangia. The seeds are oval, of the *Samaropsis* type, with a narrow wing. Their maximum breadth is 3·5 cm., and when they fell left a small cup-like depression on the margin of the under side of the pinnule.

§ *Ptychocarpus* Weiss consists of sterile and fertile pinnules which are similar in shape. Five to eight exannulate sporangia unite to form a cone-like circular synangium.

teroid pinnules which are more or less united, according to their position on the frond. The venation is distinct, the midrib being decurrent and the lateral veinlets typically bow-shaped and never divided.

Eupecopteris fletti Kidston (Plates XIV, *l*; XXVII, *e*) bears a resemblance to *Acitheca polymorpha* (Brongt.), but the lateral veinlets are less divided, the bases of the pinnules are always free (never decurrent), and the rachises bear distinct point-like marks. Among others, the last-named feature distinguishes it from *Eupecopteris pteroides* (Brongt.).

Eupecopteris cisti (Brongt.) (Plates XIV, *m*; XXVII, *h*) also has superficial affinities with *Acitheca polymorpha* and *Eupecopteris pteroides*. It is distinguished from the former by its more distant veinlets, which also take a more oblique course to the margin of the pinnule. In *E. pteroides* (Plates XIV, *n*; XXXIX, *b*) they are more oblique than in *E. cisti*, but are very much more numerous and more closely placed.

Eupecopteris camertonensis Kidston (Plates XIV, *o*; XXXI, *a*) is distinguished from *Asterotheca arborescens* (Schloth.) by its more convex pinnules, which are united by their bases and whose sides taper, while the lateral veinlets fork, whereas they are invariably undivided in *A. arborescens*.

Eupecopteris volkmanni (Sauveur) (Plates XIV, *p*; XXXI, *b*) constitutes a well-marked Yorkian species standing nearest to *Dactylotheca plumosa* (Artis), but the pinnules of the latter usually taper more gradually, while the lateral veinlets of *E. volkmanni* are bow-shaped. In *E. volkmanni*, again, the anterior and posterior basal pinnules are similar in shape, whereas they differ in *D. plumosa*.

Eupecopteris bucklandi (Brongt.) (Plates XIV, *q*; XXVII, *f*) might be mistaken for *Asterotheca oreopteridia* (Schloth.), as in both species the lateral veinlets usually fork once only. In *E. bucklandi*, however, the pinnules are contracted at the base, while in *A. oreopteridia* they are not. In the former they are about 4 mm. long, and in the latter about 5 mm. The lateral veinlets of *A. oreopteridia* usually divide once only; in the lower veinlets of the larger pinnules of *E. bucklandi* the upper arm of the fork may divide again, and the veins are more ascending than in *A. oreopteridia*. *Asterotheca miltoni* (Artis) (Plate XV, *a*) is the commonest British Pecopterid. The pinnules bear a dense covering of hairs, often obscuring the veins. The lateral veins fork once or twice. The fertile leaves are similar in shape to the barren. In the larger pinnules of the Radstockian species *A. lamuriana* (Heer) (Plate XV, *b*) the lateral veinlets fork once, but in the smaller pinnules they are undivided. *A. candolleana* (Brongt.) (Plate XV, *c*), another Radstockian form, has a smooth or longitudinally striated rachis bearing pinnules which are contracted at the base, either on one or on both sides. The veinlets leave the midrib at a very wide angle and soon fork, again forming a wide angle. *A. hemitelioides* (Brongt.) (Plate XV, *d*) has a scaly rachis and the pinnules are straight, the midrib standing at right-angles to the rachis and giving rise to straight ascending lateral veinlets which do not fork. In *A. lepidorachis* (Brongt.) (Plate XV, *e*) the rachis is dotted and the pinnules are never contracted at the base. The slightly arched lateral veinlets arise at an open angle, soon fork near the base, and one division may fork again. *Eupecopteris minor* Kidston (Plate XV, *f*), a Lanarkian form, bears small pinnules with straight margins. The veins are obscure. *Pecopteris armasi* Zeiller (Plate XV, *g*) has a longitudinally striated rachis bearing pinnules which are slightly fused at the base. No veins pass from the rachis into the pinnule (as occurs in

Alethopteris), while it is separated from *Callipteridium* by the fewer veinlets, all arising from the midrib. *P. bioti* Brongt. (Plates XV, *h*; XXXIII, *e*) is similar to *Dactylotheca plumosa*, but lateral veinlets appear to be absent and the pinnules are always entire. *P. integra* (Andrae) (Plate XV, *i*) is distinguished by the pinnules and midrib being clearly decurrent, while one edge of the pinnule curves in markedly in joining the rachis. The latter feature at once separates it from *Crossotheca pinnatafida*.

GROUP III. ALETHOPTERIDEÆ

Alethopteris aquilina (Schloth.) (Plates XVI, *a*; XXX, *c*) has pinnules measuring about 15 mm. long by 5 mm. broad, showing no tendency to enlargement in the middle, the margins being practically parallel. This at once distinguishes it from *A. serli*. The apex is bluntly pointed and the sinus between adjacent pinnules sharp. There is a very small apical pinnule (about 5–8 mm. long). The lateral veins leave the midrib at an angle of about 40 degrees and usually fork twice. There is some doubt whether *A. aquilina* (Schloth.) is identical with *A. aquilina* (Brongt.).

The Radstockian species *Alethopteris davreuxi* (Brongt.) (Plates XVI, *b*; XXX, *d*) might be mistaken for the Yorkian form *A. lonchitica* (Schloth.) (Plates XVI, *c*; XXX, *e*), but the pinnules are closer, more united, and generally not contracted at their bases, while their apices are more rounded. The lateral veinlets, which divide once or twice in both species, are more prominent and less closely placed in *A. davreuxi*, and—a very distinctive feature—are flexuous. The pinnules are from 4 to 12 mm. long and 2–3 mm. broad, while the terminal pinnule measures 7–15 mm. in length. The distinctly flexuous course of the veinlets also separates *A. davreuxi* from *A. valida* Boulay (Plates XVI, *d*; XXXVI, *n*), where they are only very slightly flexuous. In the latter species both the lateral and terminal pinnules are larger, the venation is more open, and the veinlets usually divide twice. In the very rare British species *A. integra* (Gothan) (Plate XVI, *h*) the pinnules are smaller, much more obtuse, and the veins more flexuous than in *A. valida*.

Alethopteris serli (Brongt.) (Plates XVI, *e*; XXX, *a*) has pinnules measuring 10–25 mm. long and 3–6 mm. broad, and differing from those of *A. decurrens* (Artis), *A. lonchitica* (Schloth.), *A. davreuxi* (Brongt.), and *A. valida* by their being swollen in the middle and sharper at the apex, while the lateral veinlets are finer, closer, and less divided. In this species some veinlets are undivided, others fork once, and a few twice.

Alethopteris grandini (Brongt.) (Plates XVI, *f*; XXX, *b*), with pinnules 6–25 mm. long by 4–10 mm. wide, is distinguished from *A. serli* by the pinnules being only very slightly enlarged in the middle and quite rounded at the apex, giving them an easily recognised form. The sinus separating the pinnules is markedly less sharp than in *A. serli*. Most of the veinlets in this species divide twice and are more spaced than in *A. serli*. The terminal pinnule of *A. grandini* is very characteristic; it does not exceed 10 mm. in length—with the exception of *A. aquilina*, shorter than in any species here dealt with. The rounded apex of the pinnule clearly separates it from *A. valida*.

A. grandini has also some resemblance to *A. integra* (Gothan), but in the latter the pinnules are smaller and more united (from one-quarter to one-third of their length), and the central and lateral veins take a somewhat flexuous course.

Alethopteris lonchitica (Schloth.) has been confused with *A. decurrens* (Artis) (Plates XVI, *g*; XXX, *f*). The former is the larger frond, the pinnules measuring 8–30 mm. long by 3–5 mm. broad; in *A. decurrens* they are of about the same length, but do not exceed 3 mm. in breadth. Pinnules of *A. lonchitica* tend to be oval, as there is a slight enlargement towards the middle; those of *A. decurrens* are linear. The lateral veinlets of *A. lonchitica* are finer and more closely placed; they fairly often divide twice, a feature which is not observed in *A. decurrens* (where they are either simple or fork once only). *Alethopteris gracillima* Boulay (Plate XXXVIII, *b*) is usually regarded as a form of *A. decurrens*.

Desmopteris longifolia (Sternb.) Stur (Plates XVI, *i*; XXXV, *d*) is a large frond of which only fragments are usually found. The leaflets stand almost at right-angles to the rachis and are 4–9 cm. long by 4–8 mm. wide, rounded at the base, but not stalked. The midrib is strong and slightly decurrent at the base. It gives rise at an angle of about 50 degrees to lateral veinlets which fork at about one-third of the width of the leaflet from the midrib, occasionally forking again. They are arched, especially in the lower part of the pinnule. Minute teeth occur along the margin, corresponding with the ends of the veinlets.

Lonchopteris rugosa Brongt. (Plates XVI, *j*; XXXVII, *d*) may be distinguished from *L. bricei* Brongt. (Plates XVI, *k*; XXIV, *g*; XXXVIII, *c*) by the fact that in *L. rugosa* the secondary pinnæ, being caducous, are often found detached. The polygonal meshes formed by the lateral veinlets are markedly smaller and more numerous than in *L. bricei*. *L. eschweileriana* Brongt. (Plates XVI, *l*; XXIV, *h*) has larger and fewer meshes than *L. bricei*.

GROUP IV. NEUROPTERIDEÆ

Callipteridium gigas (Gutbier) (Plates XVII, *a*; XXXI, *c, d*) is a rare Radstockian species. The sessile pinnules are attached almost at right-angles to the rachis and are not, or only very slightly, decurrent (contrast species of *Alethopteris*). They are slightly united at the base, and their lateral margins touch up to about two-thirds of their length. There is a distinct midrib as far as two-thirds up the pinnule (contrast *Odontopteris*), after which it breaks up into forking veinlets. The lateral veinlets are numerous and closely placed, arising at an angle of 30–50 degrees, and forking several times at an acute angle. In the lower part of the pinnule veinlets enter the leaf directly from the rachis, a condition found in *Alethopteris* but not in Pecopterids.

Linopteris münsteri (Eichwald) (Plates XVII, *b*; XXXI, *i*) has pinnules of the same shape as those of *Neuropteris heterophylla* Brongt., but is easily recognised by the lateral veinlets forming a network. The meshes are markedly larger and fewer than in *L. obliqua* Bunbury (Plates XVII, *d*; XXXVII, *c*), which is a homœomorph of *Neuropteris gigantea* Sternb. (Plates XVII, *e*; XXVIII, *f*). As in *N. gigantea* and some other species of *Neuropteris*, the pinnules of *L. obliqua* were caducous, and are therefore often found detached.

In *Neuropteris obliqua* (Brongt.) (Plates XVII, *f*; XXIII, *j*), while the lower margin of the pinnules tends to be decurrent down the rachis, the upper contracts, resulting in a broad junction of the pinnule with the rachis. The pinnules are oval or linear-lanceolate, with rounded apices, and the terminal pinnule (which also has a rounded apex) is longer than the others. Characteristic features are the slightly decurrent base of the midrib and the flexuous, even undulating, course of the lateral veinlets. The veinlets are more flexuous, more ascending, and more divided than in *N. schlehani* (Plates XVIII, *a*; XXVIII, *c*). They are fewer and stronger than in *N. tenuifolia* (Schloth.) (Plates XVII, *g*; XXVIII, *h*), in which the base of the pinnules is clearly contracted on both sides. In *Neuropteris heterophylla* Brongt. (Plates XVII, *c*; XXIX, *h*), with pinnules contracted at the base, the veinlets are stronger and much more numerous than in *N. obliqua*. *N. obliqua* forma *impar* Weiss, sometimes regarded as a separate species, is shown on Plate XXVIII, *a*.

Neuropteris fimbriata Lesqx. (Plate XXVIII, *b*) has oval or oblong pinnules which are generally fringed from the middle to the apex and which are attached to the rachis by a broad base. The delicate leaf shows numerous distinct veinlets radiating from the base and generally forking twice. This species differs from *N. dentata* Lesqx. only in the venation; in the latter species the veins are fine, closely placed, and slightly arched.

Neuropteris schlehani Stur is characterised by its oval stalked pinnules having distinctly arched (not straight) margins and obtuse apices. They touch or even overlap each other, and are 3–20 mm. long by 2–6 mm. broad. Another typical feature is the linear terminal pinnule, which is longer than the others and has an obtuse apex. The lateral veinlets are clearly marked and project slightly above the surface of the leaf. They arch very rapidly after leaving the midrib and fork two or three times, giving rise to a series of closely placed veinlets. The contraction of the base of the pinnule, the arched margins, and the absence of flexuous lateral veinlets separates *N. schlehani* from *N. obliqua*. In *N. rarinervis* (Plates XVIII, *b*; XXV, *k*) the veinlets are markedly thicker and fewer, while in *N. tenuifolia* the pinnules are larger, the margins less arched, and the veins finer.

Neuropteris scheuchzeri Hoffmann (Plates XVII, *h*; XXVIII, *d*) is distinguished from other species of *Neuropteris* by its pointed pinnules which have a distinctly hairy surface. The hairs may be mistaken for veins. *N. acuminata* (Schloth.) sometimes also has pointed pinnules, but hairs are absent from this species, the pinnules are broader in proportion to their length, the veinlets are much more flexuous, and where a small basal pinnule exists it occurs on the lower side of the pinnule only—*N. scheuchzeri* generally bears two basal pinnules, one on each side.

Neuropteris flexuosa Sternb. (Plates XVIII, *d*; XXVIII, *e*) and *N. ovata* Hoffmann (Plates XVIII, *c*; XXVIII, *g*) are very similar, *N. flexuosa* being the larger. Except for a few upper pinnules, which are attached by their whole base, the base of the pinnule is distinctly contracted in both species. In *N. flexuosa* the terminal pinnule is enlarged and free, but in *N. ovata* it is small and united by the base to the uppermost pinnule or pinnules. The pinnules of *N. flexuosa* overlap more than those of *N. ovata* (which may touch by their margins). The lateral veinlets of *N. flexuosa* are fewer and less arched than those of *N. ovata*.

Neuropteris gigantea Sternb. (Plates XVII, *e*; XXVIII, *f*) had pinnules which were easily shed and are often found isolated. Their lateral margins are fairly straight and their apices rounded. A typical feature is that the terminal pinnule is smaller than the others. The veinlets are very fine and very closely placed. The pinnules and veinlets are closer than in *N. flexuosa*.

Neuropteris tenuifolia (Schloth.) (Plates XVII, *g*; XXVIII, *h*) has pinnules 5–20 mm. long by 1–5 mm. wide, the margins of which are parallel or slightly converging towards the rounded apex. The terminal pinnule is larger than the others and, like them, contracted at the base. The midrib can be seen for about two-thirds up the pinnule. The lateral veinlets are characteristically fine and well spaced. Compared with *N. heterophylla* the pinnules are longer in proportion to their breadth and more tapering towards the apex, while the veinlets are fewer, finer, and less close. In *N. rarinervis*, on the other hand, the veinlets are markedly fewer, much thicker, and more distinctly arched. From *N. obliqua*, *N. tenuifolia* is distinguished by the contracted base of the pinnules, and by the fact that the veinlets are closer and less forked.

Neuropteris microphylla Brongt. (Plates XVIII, *g*; XXVIII, *i*) has small oval pinnules with very rounded apices, 5–6 mm. long by 3–4 mm. broad. The base is broad and the veinlets few. The shape and size of the pinnules readily distinguish this species.

Neuropteris macrophylla Brongt. (Plates XVII, *i*; XXIX, *g*) stands nearest to *N. osmundæ* (Artis) (= *N. auriculata* Brongt.), with pinnules of similar shape but in which the veins are more closely placed. The base of the pinnules may have ear-like appendages. There is also some similarity to *N. scheuchzeri*, but, while large cyclopteroid pinnules may occur on the rachis of *N. macrophylla*, the small cyclopteroid pinnules at the base of the terminal lobe so often seen in *N. scheuchzeri* are absent from *N. macrophylla*. The surface of the pinnules of *N. macrophylla* is not hairy. In *N. macrophylla* the lateral veins usually fork four times, the last fork occurring near the margin—much closer than in *N. scheuchzeri*, where the veins are also closer.

Neuropteris osmundæ (Artis), though rare on any horizon, is most frequent in the Yorkian Series. It is identical with *N. auriculata* Brongt. and *N. villiersii* Brongt. The large pinnules are of unequal size and variable in shape, entire, with serrated margins and bluntly rounded apices. As observed above, the base of the pinnules may be eared. The central vein is very weak, and soon breaks up into lateral veins which arch slightly and fork three or four times. Mr. Hemingway suggests that *N. osmundæ* may eventually prove to be a basal portion of *N. obliqua*.

In *Neuropteris heterophylla* Brongt. the pinnules are 5–20 mm. long by 3–8 mm. wide; they are sessile and rounded at the apex, and the terminal pinnule is larger than the others. The midrib is strong at the base and divides into many rather closely placed veinlets which are well marked. The veinlets are fewer and stronger than in *N. gigantea*. The pinnules are shorter in proportion to their length than in *N. tenuifolia*, less tapering at the apex, and the veinlets are stronger. In *N. schlehani* the leaflets are straighter and the veinlets more separated, while the terminal pinnule is characteristically linear. In *N. obliqua*, finally, the pinnules are usually united to the rachis by a broad base, and the veinlets are more flexuous and fewer.

Neuropteris rectinervis Kidston (Plates XVIII, *e*; XXIII, *k*; XXIX, *i*) appears to merge into *N. schlehani* on the one hand and *Alethopteris lonchitica* on the other. In shape the pinnules are Neuropteroid, but the venation is Alethopteroid. The pinnules are sessile, oval or oblong, with blunt apices. The margin is entire and the midrib extends almost to the apex. There are numerous distinct fine lateral veinlets which spring from the midrib with a gentle curve, after which they pursue a course almost at right-angles to the margin of the pinnule. They usually fork once, occasionally twice. The terminal pinnule is oblong. In the somewhat similar *N. kosmanni* Arber (?) Potonié the pinnules are larger and the lateral veins stand at an acute angle to the midrib.

Neuropteris rarinervis Bunbury has small pinnules with slightly enlarged bases. The margins gradually taper towards the apex and the terminal pinnules are larger than the others. The midrib is strongly marked and continues almost to the apex, dividing into a few strong veinlets which are well separated and strongly arched. Compared with *N. heterophylla* the veinlets are stronger, more arched, and fewer, while the pinnules are smaller. *N. schlehani*, on the other hand, is distinguished by the linear terminal pinnule and the much more numerous and finer veinlets.

Neuropteris grangeri Brongt. (Plates XVIII, *f*; XXIII, *h, i*) may have shortly stalked or sessile pinnules measuring from 8–18 mm. in length by 5–12 mm. broad at the widest point (the base). They become slightly narrower towards the apex and end in an obtuse point. The midrib is immersed in the tissue of the pinnule and gives rise to clearly marked lateral veinlets which generally fork twice. In *N. blissi* Lesqx. (Plate XVIII, *j*) the lanceolate pinnules are often sickle-shaped, and the very fine lateral veinlets arise at a sharp angle and curve gently outwards, forking to form about eight veinlets. *N. crenulata* Brongt. (Plate XVIII, *k*), a Lanarkian species, is characterised by the crenulate margin of its pinnules. *N. carpentieri* Kidston (Plate XVIII, *l*) appears to include the microsporophylls of some species of *Neuropteris*. A sterile pinnule is figured.

Odontopteris lindleyana Sternb. (Plates XVIII, *h*; XXIX, *e*) is a very distinctive type of leaf. The pinnules are given off at an angle of about 45 degrees and are about 1 cm. long by 0·5 cm. broad. *Odontopteris britannica* Gutbier (Plates XVIII, *i*; XXIX, *f*), as recorded from Britain, is a form of *Neuropteris diversifolia* Gothan and Jongmans (which has been separated from forms hitherto included under *N. obliqua*).* The widely placed veins which arise from the rachis gives it some resemblance to *O. lindleyana*, but the ends are continued as long spine-like processes.

The various records of *Odontopteris alpina* (Presl) from the Staffordian and Yorkian Series of Britain require confirmation. Some of these specimens appear to represent portions of a frond of *Neuropteris heterophylla*, or of some closely related species.

FILICALES AND PTERIDOSPERMEÆ INCERTÆ SEDIS

Aphlebia spinosa Lesqx. (Plate XXIX, *d*) has a broad flat membranous rachis which gives rise to alternate pinnules at an acute angle. The pinnules have two or three short spine-like teeth and a prominent lanceolate terminal lobe. Along the centre of the rachis is a vein which gives rise to simple veins, one going to each pinnule. The rachis may or may not bear point-like marks.

Aphlebia crispa (Gutbier) (Plate XXX, *g*) is one of the larger types of

---

* This statement is based on information, as yet unpublished, kindly supplied by Professor Jongmans.

Aphlebiæ. The pinnate leaf attains a length of nearly 60 cm. and is divided into deeply lobed segments. *A. linearis* (Gutbier) (Plate XXVI, *c*) is common in the Yorkian Series.

Cyclopteris reniformis Brongt. (Plate XXIX, *a*) is a kidney-shaped entire pinnule with slightly undulating margins; the veins are simple at the base and subdivide in the lamina, arching and distant. The base of the pinnule is deeply indented. *C. orbicularis* Brongt. (Plate XXIX, *b*) is probably identical with *C. trichomanoides* Sternb. The shape of these pinnules varies with their position on the frond. A further example of a *Cyclopteris* pinnule is given on Plate XXIX, *c*.

Spiropteris is shown on Plate XXVI, *g*. It may be pointed out that the young leaves of Angiosperms do not show the crosier-like arrangement ("circinate vernation") seen in ferns (both extinct and recent) and in Pteridosperms.

Three figures showing casts of the stems of tree-ferns are given. *Caulopteris anglica* Kidston (Plate XXXVI, *a*) bears closely placed, spirally arranged leaf-scars, within each of which is an oval or U-shaped leaf-trace scar. *Megaphyton frondosum* Artis (Plate XXXVIII, *a*), another cast of the outer surface of these stems, has two vertical rows of larger oval scars, and it is evident that the leaves on one side of the stem alternated with those on the other. Among recent tree-ferns the leaves may be arranged on the erect stems as in *Caulopteris*, but the distichous arrangement seen in *Megaphyton* is unrepresented except on rhizomes. In the latter genus the leaf-trace scar takes the form of a closed ring, the base of which is an inverted U. *Ptychopteris* (Plate XXXV, *a*) includes decorticated examples which show the exposed vascular system of the stem; the leaf scars may be of either the *Caulopteris* or the *Megaphyton* type. That figured illustrates the latter arrangement. In *Caulopteris* and *Megaphyton* the impressions of roots may be seen between the leaf-scars.

CHAPTER VII

GYMNOSPERMOUS SEEDS

As observed above, many Gymnospermous seeds are found in the Coal Measures. They usually occur detached, and belong to either the Pteridosperms or the Cordaitales.

Neuropterocarpus sp. (Plate XXXVI, *h*) is the seed of the Pteridosperms *Neuropteris heterophylla* and *N. obliqua* (note in the figure the leaflet of *N. heterophylla* attached close to the base of the seed, on the left-hand side). Kidston originally referred these seeds to *Rhabdocarpus*, a much misunderstood genus which differs from *Cordaicarpus* in the seeds being always longer than broad and in their having no basal indentation. In 1914 Arber removed the *Neuropteris* seeds to *Neurospermum*, but Grand 'Eury's genus *Neuropterocarpus* has priority. There is a great similarity between the impressions referred to *Neuropterocarpus* and the form of the structural seeds called *Trigonocarpus shorensis* Salisbury, which occur associated with petioles of *Myeloxylon*.

Trigonocarpus parkinsoni Brongt. (Plate XXXVI, *d*, *e*) is a common seed of the British Coal Measures, being fairly frequent in the Yorkian, though less common in the Lanarkian Series. It is so often associated with the impressions of leaves *Alethopteris lonchitica* (the foliage of the Pteridosperm *Medullosa anglica*) that there is little doubt as to its being the seed of that plant, a view which is supported by certain structural features. The genus *Trigonocarpus* includes fairly large seeds which are oval, longer than broad, unsymmetrically winged, the apex being produced into a micropyle. The testa is differentiated into a soft outer sarcotesta and a hard inner sclerotesta. The inner surface of the latter bore three longitudinal equidistant grooves. Impressions of the outer surface of *T. parkinsoni* were distinguished by Lindley and Hutton (*Fossil Flora*, vol. ii, Plate lxxxvii, Figs. 1–3) as *Carpolithus alatus*. Impressions of the sclerotesta and micropyle were named *Rhabdocarpus bochschianus* by Berger, while the commonest forms of fossilisation of the seed, representing three-ridged casts of the inner surface of the sclerotesta, as here figured, were called *Trigonocarpus nœggerathi* by Lindley and Hutton (*Fossil Flora*, vol. ii, Plate cxlii, Figs. 1–3). (*T. nœggerathi* L. and H. is distinct from *T. nœggerathi* Sternberg.) In the first two forms of preservation the seed is oval and smooth. The casts are ovoid, with a pointed apex and rounded base, 1·8 to 2·8 cm. long and up to 1·5 cm. broad. *Trigonocarpus olivæformis* L. and H. and *T. oblongus* L. and H. are also different states of preservation of this seed, while *T. dawsei* L. and H. is the cast of a seed cavity resembling those of *T. parkinsoni*, but measuring 4·5 cm. in length by 2·5 cm. in breadth.

Trigonocarpus nœggerathi (Sternb. *non* L. and H.) (Plate XXXVI, *i*), like *T. parkinsoni*, is radially symmetrical. It measures 2·5–4·0 cm. in length by 1–3 cm. in breadth. The base is rounded and the apex bluntly pointed. There are three prominent longitudinal ridges, between which the surface is smooth. The seed is often split into three valves along the angles of the triangle formed by the ridges. This is probably the fruit of a Radstockian species of *Alethopteris*, i.e. of a Pteridosperm.

Cordaicarpus crassus (Lesqx.) (Plate XXXVI, *g*) is an oval seed about 1 cm. long. The nucule is ovate and the wing forms a narrow border equidistant round it. The micropyle ends in a point. In this genus are placed impressions of circular or oval seeds which have an external resemblance to those seeds showing structure known as *Cardiocarpus*. *Samaropsis* seeds which had lost their border (or which showed only a narrow border) would be referred to *Cordaicarpus*, which is therefore only a provisional genus. Some species of *Cordaicarpus* belong to the Cordaitales; others almost certainly belong to Pteridosperms. *C. cordai* (Geinitz) (Plate XXXIII, *i*) was once thought to have been borne by *Cordaites principalis*, though this is improbable. The seed is circular or ovate, 8–20 mm. in diameter, with a slightly heart-shaped base and a very gradually tapering apex. The border may be absent and in any case is very narrow. Faint longitudinal striations may occur on the surface, which is, however, more often quite smooth. This species has been confused with *Carpolithus membranaceus*.

The genus *Samaropsis* Goeppert includes casts or impressions of flat, more or less circular (never longer than broad) Palæozoic seeds. They differ from *Cordaicarpus* Geinitz in posssesing a definite border or wing (the sarcotesta). The sclerotesta is heart-shaped or egg-shaped, and the micropyle fairly long. Impressions of these seeds preserved as mummified tissue in wet clays can be removed with the point of a knife, and often show well-preserved tissue under the microscope. *Samaropsis* seeds were probably borne by certain of the Cordaitales (e.g. probably by *Dorycordaites palmæformis* and possibly by *Cordaites principalis*), and certainly by some Pteridosperms (e.g. by *Dicksonites pluckeneti* or the very similar *Pecopteris sterzeliana* and probably by *Eremopteris artemisæfolia*). *S. reniformis* (Geinitz) (Plate XXXIII, *j*) is a kidney-shaped seed, 2·3 cm. broad by 1·9 cm. long. The border is clearly shown, 3–4 mm. wide. In *Cordaicarpus gutbieri* (Geinitz), which has been confused with *S. reniformis*, the wing is distinctly narrower and the seed is longer in proportion to its width.

Samaropsis quadriovata Kidston (Plate XXXVIII, *i*) is quadrate-oval, 9 mm. long by 7 mm. wide. The border is very narrow at the base but widens considerably towards the apex, where it attains a width of 2 mm. The nucule is heart-shaped with an acute apex. It occurs only in the Yorkian Series, where it is very rare. *S. acuta* (L. and H.) (Plate XXXVI, *m*) is probably the seed of the Pteridosperm *Eremopteris artemisæfolia*. It varies considerably in size, but average specimens measure 1 cm. in length by 0·7 cm. in width. In shape it is from elliptical to circular. The wing, which is longitudinally striated, is very narrow at the base and gradually expands towards the apex, where it attains about 1 mm. across. The actual apex seems to possess a single sharp point in young seeds, but in mature specimens it is notched and there are two sharp forward directed points. The longitudinal ridge running down the centre of the seed represents the vascular strand.

Samaropsis orbicularis Ett. (Plate XXXVIII, *d*) is circular or oval, broader

Samaropsis orbicularis Ett. (Plate **XXXVIII**, *d*) is circular or oval, broader than long. The length is about 1 cm. and the breadth 1·3 cm. The border does not exceed 1 mm. in width. The surface of the bluntly pointed nucule is smooth. It may here be pointed out that the British seeds which at various times and by various authors have been referred to *Samaropsis* (*Cardiocarpum*) *fluitans* Dawson require revision. They undoubtedly represent more than one species, and, as Dawson's description of his species is unsatisfactory, it is doubtful if any can be identified with *S. fluitans*.

Holcospermum mammillatum (Lesqx.) (Plate **XXXVI**, *b*). Many of the seeds placed in Nathorst's genus *Holcospermum* were originally included in *Rhabdocarpus* (which is now reserved for unsymmetrical examples of the *R. tunicatus* Berger type). Arber separated other Rhabdocarpi under the new designation *Platyspermum*, regarding them as flat, but the symmetry of these seeds is often in doubt, and they are best referred to *Holcospermum*, which includes either flat or radially symmetrical seeds with prominent sharp or rounded ridges (depending on the state of preservation) traversing their entire length. In *H. mammillatum* the seeds are symmetrical, 12–13 mm. long by 6–7 mm. broad. The testa bears prominent longitudinal ridges traversing the whole length of the seed and taking a slightly flexuous course. The apex typically ends in a little mammillate point, and this gave rise to the specific name. It is not shown, however, on all Lesqureux's figures. On the grounds of association, I believe this to be the Pteridospermous seed of a species of *Neuropteris*, probably of *N. scheuchzeri* Hoffmann.

Holcospermum elongatum (Kidston) (Plate **XXXVI**, *j*) is narrow, up to 2·5 cm. long by 3·5 cm. wide. The testa bears four or more longitudinal ridges on each side. The base and apex gradually taper, but in imperfectly preserved examples the apex may appear rounded.

Mr. Hemingway has made the interesting suggestion that *H. elongatum* is not a seed, but that it represents some type of spore-bearing capsule. It is difficult to be sure which is the apex and which the base of the specimens.

The genus *Carpolithus* Linnæus (sometimes spelt *Carpolithes*) includes casts and impressions of detached seeds, both large and small, which, lacking regular ribbing or other distinguishing features, cannot be assigned to the more clearly defined genera. Some belong to Pteridosperms, others to the Cordaitales. *C. membranaceus* Goeppert (Plate **XXXV**, *b*) has often been united to *C.* (*Rhabdocarpus*) *ovoideus* Goeppert and Berger, but, whereas the former appears smooth, the latter bears fine striæ, representing sclerenchymatous fibres which occurred in the pericarp. The species has also been confused with *Cordaicarpus cordai* (Plate **XXXIII**, *i*), and many specimens figured as *C. cordai* by Kidston and others belong to *C. membranaceus*. The surface of *C. cordai* is generally smooth, though it may bear fine longitudinal striations; that of *C. membranaceus* may appear smooth to the naked eye, but under the lens it is seen to consist of a regular meshwork of thick-walled hexagonal cells. *C. membranaceus* varies in shape from circular to oval, the circular specimens attaining a diameter of about 0·8 cm. and the oval measuring up to 1 cm. in length by 0·75 cm. in breadth. Occasionally the apex, and rarely the base, is bluntly pointed. The appearance of a border which sometimes occurs, suggesting a *Samaropsis*, is not an original feature; it has been caused by crushing during fossilisation.

Carpolithus regularis Sternb. (Plate **XXXVIII**, *h*) is a small seed occurring very rarely in the Yorkian Series only. It is oval, bluntly pointed at base and apex, measuring about 9 mm. long by 6 mm. broad, smooth, and surrounded by a narrow border. *C. regularis* has been united with *C. ovoideus* Goepp. and Berger, a very similar type, which, however, has a striated surface. *C. regularis* is more oval than *C. membranaceus* and possesses a more definite border (which may have the same origin as in that species).

Carpolithus areolatus (Boulay) (Plate **XXXVI**, *f*) is sometimes placed in the genus *Cordaicarpus*. It is small and oval, the longer axis measuring 4–6 mm. The base is rounded and the apex may be bluntly pointed. The outer surface bears an irregular network of meshes, regarded by some as representing ridges in the outer surface of the pericarp, but in some instances at least being due to the splitting of the carbonised layer. It has been suggested, on the grounds of association, that this seed belongs to *Cordaites borassifolius* (Sternb.), but no connection between the parts has been seen.

Carpolithus inflatus (Lesqx.) (Plate **XXXVI**, *c*) is often placed in the genus *Rhabdocarpus*, as the seed sometimes bears longitudinal bands. As a rule, however, the testa bears no ribs or striæ, though it is irregularly wrinkled. The seed is large, up to 4 cm. long, ovoid, the base rounded, and the apex bluntly pointed. It is fairly rare in the Yorkian and very rare in the Lanarkian Series.

CHAPTER VIII

COAL MEASURE FLORAS

Dr. Kidston often pointed out that the plant divisions of the British Coal Measures cannot be recognised by the presence or absence of any one species, but that it is essential to take into account the entire known flora of the beds under investigation. Besides drawing up a list of zonal plants, the frequency with which each species occurs should be noted, as occasionally a plant typical of the Radstockian Series may be found in Yorkian rocks, or a Yorkian plant in Radstockian beds, but in such cases it is usually characteristically common in one division and extremely rare in the other. Species vary considerably in zonal value.

(1) *THE RADSTOCKIAN FLORA*

The Radstockian flora consists mainly of the *Cyatheites-Pecopterids*, the commonest examples of which are *Acitheca polymorpha*, *Asterotheca abbreviata*, *A. arborescens*, *A. cyathea*, *A. oreopteridia*, *Ptychocarpus unitus*, and *Eupecoperis dentata*, while among the rarer species *Asterotheca daubreei*, *Dicksonites pluckeneti*, *Eupecopteris camertonensis*, *E. cisti*, and *E. fletti* may be cited. The most frequent *Sphenopterideæ* are *Crossotheca pinnatafida*, *Sphenopteris alata*, *S. macilenta*, and *S. neuropteroides*. *Alethopteris serli* is very common, but *A. grandini*, *A. aquilina*, and *A. davreuxi*, though characteristic, are rare. *Desmopteris longifolia* and *Callipteridium gigas* are rare. Radstockian species of *Neuropteris* are *N. ovata*, *N. flexuosa*, *N. macrophylla*, *N. rarinervis*, *N. scheuchzeri*, and *N. fimbriata*, while *Odontopteris lindleyana* is a typical fossil. *Aphlebia crispa* and *A. filiciformis*, as well as species of *Caulopteris* and *Megaphyton* are found. *Trigonocarpus næggerathi* is the most frequent seed.

Of the Equisetales, the pith-casts known as *Calamites suckowi* and *C. carinatus* and the leafy branches called *Asterophyllites equisetiformis* occur (though they are not characteristic forms), but *Annularia stellata* and *A. sphenophylloides* are typical leaves. Calamitic cones are rare, the most frequent being *Macrostachya infundibuliformis*. Among the Sphenophyllales, *Sphenophyllum emarginatum* is a very common type of foliage.

Lepidodendron wortheni, *L. lanceolatum*, and *Sigillaria lævigata* and *S.*

cumulata are fairly common. *Cordaites angulosostriatus* is very common, but *C. borassifolius* and *Poacordaites microstachys* are very rare. The two British species of *Walchia* (*W. imbricata* and *W. piniformis*) are very rare

(2) *THE STAFFORDIAN FLORA*

The Staffordian flora is intermediate between the Radstockian and Yorkian floras. The uppermost rocks, the Newcastle-under-Lyme Group, contain a predominance of Radstockian species, with the slight admixture of Yorkian forms, while the reverse is the case with the lowest beds, the Blackband Group. The central group, which is very barren of fossils, is known as the Etruria Marl Group. Certain species of *Neuropteris* (*N. scheuchzeri* and *N. rarinervis*) are as common in the Newcastle-under-Lyme Group as in the Radstockian Series, but there is a considerable diminution in the number of Pecopterids present.

(3) *THE YORKIAN FLORA*

This is the richest of the Coal Measure floras. As in the Radstockian Series, the Filicales and Pteridospermeæ provide the bulk of the species, but the *Cyatheites-Pecopterids* are here rare and the *Sphenopterideæ* very common. Typical examples of the last-named group are *Corynepteris coralloides*, *Diplotmema furcatum*, *Renaultia rotundifolia*, *Senftenbergia ophiodermatica*, *Sphenopteris dilatata*, *S. laurenti*, *S. sauveuri*, *S. schatzlarensis*, *S. spiniformis*, *S. striata*, *S. trifoliolata*, and *Mariopteris nervosa*. The Yorkian *Pecopterideæ* include *Dactylotheca plumosa* and *Eupecopteris volkmanni*. *Neuropteris* is represented by *N. heterophylla*, *N. gigantea*, *N. tenuifolia*, *N. obliqua*, *N grangeri*, and *N. microphylla*. *Alethopteris decurrens* and *A. lonchitica* are common to both the Yorkian and Lanarkian, while species of *Lonchopteris* and *Linopteris*, though not common, are mainly found in the Yorkian. *Aphlebia linearis* is very common.

Turning to the Equisetales, the following stems are found: *Calamites suckowi*, *C. carinatus*, *C. schützeiformis*, *C. undulatus*, *C. cisti*, and *C. gœpperti*, while the leaves and leafy branches are referred to *Annularia radiata*, *A. dubia*, *Asterophyllites equisetiformis*, and *A. charæformis*. The commonest Calamitic cones are *Palæostachya pedunculata* and *P. ettingshauseni*.

Specimens of *Sphenophyllum cuneifolium*, *S. saxifragæfolium*, and *S. trichomatosum* are fairly common.

The Lycopodiales are well represented in this division. There are a number of species of *Lepidodendron* (*L. aculeatum*, *L. acutum*, *L. lycopodioides*, *L. obovatum*, *L. ophiurus*, *L. simile*, *L. loricatum*, and *L. sub-wortheni*), of

Sigillaria (*S. discophora*, *S. lævigata*, *S. mammillaris*, *S. rugosa*, *S. tessellata*, *S. elongata*, *S. principis*, and *S. scutellata*), and a few rarer examples of the genera *Lepidophloios* (*L. laricinus*, *L. acerosus*), *Bothrodendron* (*B. minutifolium*, *B. punctatum*), and *Pinakodendron* (*P. macconochiei*). *Stigmaria ficoides* is common and ubiquitous

In this flora the Cordaitales are mainly represented by *Cordaites principalis*, *C. borassifolius*, and *Dorycordaites palmæformis*. *Samaropsis acuta* is the detached seed of the fructification known as *Cordaianthus pitcairniæ*, and, apart from this, the most frequent Gymnospermous seeds are *Trigonocarpus parkinsoni*, *Samaropsis meachemi*, *Holcospermum elongatum*, and *Carpolithus membranaceus*.

(4) THE LANARKIAN FLORA

Certain species are confined to Lanarkian rocks, but most Lanarkian plants are also found in the Yorkian, where, however, they are usually much commoner and are accompanied by many other forms which do not occur in the Lanarkian. Among the Pteridosperms and Filicales are found *Sphenopteris striata*, *Diplotmema furcatum*, *Eremopteris artemisæfolia*, *Renaultia gracilis*, *Urnatopteris tenella*, *Mariopteris nervosa*, *Alethopteris decurrens*, *A. lonchitica*, *Neuropteris heterophylla*, and *N. rectinervis*.

The most frequent Calamitic stems are *Calamites suckowi*, *C. carinatus*, and *C. undulatus*, and these are accompanied by the leaves *Annularia radiata* and *Asterophyllites equisetiformis*, and the cone *Palæostachya pedunculata*. The species of *Sphenophyllum* occurring are *S. cuneifolium* and *S. saxifragæfolium*. The Lycopodiales are represented by *Lepidodendron ophiurus*, *L. aculeatum*, *L. obovatum*, *Sigillaria discophora*, *S. elegans*, *S. scutellata*, and *Lepidophloios acerosus*, and the Cordaitales by the leaves *Cordaites principalis*. The commonest seed is *Samaropsis acuta*.

The relative frequency of the various groups of British Coal Measure plants in the Radstockian, Staffordian, Yorkian, and Lanarkian divisions is illustrated diagrammatically on Plate II. This refers to incrustations only, and, in some measure, takes into account both the presence of a species in a division and the frequency with which it occurs.

APPENDIX

PRACTICAL SUGGESTIONS

(1) *Collect* fully from any given locality or horizon: it requires at least twelve to twenty visits to obtain anything approaching a representative flora, and one locality or horizon investigated thoroughly is of more value than a number superficially treated. Specimens from known horizons (a particular coal seam or other information indicating the exact position of the beds) are of greater geological value than those from tip-heaps, though the latter may have geological value, especially if preserved in a characteristic rock, or if a few seams only are worked. Collect small and fragmentary as well as large showy specimens—especially cones, seeds, and fern-like leaves bearing sporangia.

(2) *Label* each specimen at the very first opportunity, using a little croid or seccotine and writing with good (preferably Indian) ink. State (*a*) the horizon, if known, and (*b*) the exact locality—name of pit or quarry, position of section or outcrop, etc. The label should be on the back of the specimen.

(3) *Pack* specimens singly and tightly in paper to prevent rubbing and consequent spoiling of surface of fossil.

(4) Do *not varnish* specimens: if it is necessary to mend a specimen, use a little croid or seccotine and tie with string until dry.

(5) Examples of *Sigillaria* and *Lepidodendron* are often found in which the scars are obscured by a thin coaly layer: they are often excellently preserved, and only require slow heating in a red fire to burn off the coal.

(6) *In identifying*, make use of specimens exhibited in the larger Museums, comparing the descriptions with these as well as with the figures. The Kidston Collection of fossil plants, preserved in the Museum of Practical Geology, Jermyn Street, is probably the finest in the world.

(7) *Preserve* specimens by presenting them to public Museums where they can be examined by other workers, the indentifications checked and possibly fresh facts brought to light. Unless the identifications can be confirmed records are of little value and must often be ignored altogether.

LIST OF SPECIES DESCRIBED, FIGURED, OR MENTIONED

Roman numerals refer to plates, Arabic numerals to pages of the text, the chief page reference being marked by an asterisk.

Acitheca polymorpha (Brongniart),[1] XIV, *a*; XXVI, *f*; 54*, 56, 67
Alethopteris aquilina (Schlotheim), XVI, *a*; XXX, *c*; 57*, 67
,, *davreuxi* (Brongniart), XVI, *b*; XXX, *d*; 57*, 67
,, *decurrens* (Artis), XVI, *g*; XXX, *f*; 57, 58*, 68, 69
,, *gracillima* Boulay, XXXVIII, *b*; 58
,, *grandini* (Brongniart), XVI, *f*; XXX, *b*; 57*, 67
,, *integra* (Gothan), XVI, *h*; 57
,, *lonchitica* (Schlotheim), XVI, *c*; XXX, *e*; 47, 48, 57, 58*, 60, 63, 68, 69
,, *serli* (Brongniart), XVI, *e*; XXX, *a*; 47, 57*, 67
,, *valida* Boulay, XVI, *d*; XXXVI, *n*; 57
Alloiopteris radstockensis Kidston, XIII, *e*; 53
,, *serrula* (Lesquereux), XIII, *d*; 53
Annularia dubia (Sternberg), 68
,, *galioides* (Lindley and Hutton), X, *k*; 41
,, *microphylla* Sauveur, X, *j*; XXV, *a*; 41
,, *radiata* Brongniart, X, *m*; XXV, *b*; 21, 41*, 68, 69
,, *sphenophylloides* (Zenker), X, *n*; XXV, *f*; 42*, 67
,, *stellata* (Schlotheim), X, *l*; XXV, *h*; 41*, 42, 67
Aphlebia crispa (Gutbier), XXX, *g*; 61*, 67
,, *filiciformis* (Gutbier), 67
,, *linearis* (Gutbier), XXVI, *c*; 62, 68

Aphlebia spinosa Lesquereux, XXIX, *d*; 61*
Asolanus camptotænia Wood, III, *n*; XXI, *c*; 26
Asterophyllites charæformis (Sternberg), X, *p*; XXV, *e*; 41, 42*, 68
,, *equisetiformis* (Schlotheim), X, *o*; XXV, *c*; 42*, 67, 68, 69
,, *grandis* (Sternberg), X, *q*; 42
,, *longifolius* (Sternberg), X, *r*; 42
Asterotheca abbreviata (Brongniart), XIV, *b*; XXVI, *d*; 54*, 67
,, *arborescens* (Schlotheim), XIV, *g*; XXVI, *a*; 55, 56*, 67
,, *candolleana* (Brongniart), XV, *c*; 56
,, *crenulata* (Brongniart), XIV, *e*; XXVII, *a*; 55
,, *cyathea* (Schlotheim), XIV, *f*; XXVII, *c*; 55*, 67
,, *daubreei* (Zeiller), XIV, *d*; XXVII, *d*; 54*, 67
,, *hemitelioides* (Brongniart), XV, *d*; 56
,, *lamuriana* (Heer), XV, *b*; 56
,, *lepidorachis* (Brongniart), XV, *e*; 56
,, *miltoni* (Artis), XV, *a*; 56
,, *oreopteridia* (Schlotheim), XIV, *c*; XXVII, *g*; 54*, 56, 67 ·

Bothrodendron minutifolium (Boulay), V, *c*; XXII, *h*; 24, 26*, 69
,, *punctatum* Lindley and Hutton, III, *m*; 26*, 27, 69

[1] The names of authors of species, frequently abbreviated in the text, are here given in full. Where an author's name is placed in a bracket, this indicates that the species was described by that author under another generic name and that subsequent work has shown the necessity of placing it in the present genus. When the word "*pars*" follows an author's name, this indicates that not all the figured specimens originally included by the author in describing his species are now regarded as typical of that species; in other words, more than one species was figured under the original specific name.

Lepidodendron obovatum Sternberg, III, *i*;
    XXI, *e*; 21, 25*, 68, 69
    „   *ophiurus* (Brongniart), III, *d*;
        IV, *c*; XX, *c*; 24*, 68,
        69
    „   *peachi* Kidston, VI, *e*; 25
    „   *rimosum* Sternberg, III, *j*;
        XXXVII, *f*; 25
    „   *serpentigerum* Koenig, 25
    „   *simile* Kidston, III, *e*; IV, *d*;
        XX, *d*; 24*, 68
    „   *sub-wortheni* Hemingway
        MS., 68
    „   *veltheimianum* Sternberg, 25
    „   *wedekindi* Weiss, 25
    „   *wortheni* Lesquereux, III, *g*;
        V, *b*; XX, *g*; 25*, 67
Lepidophloios acerosus (Lindley and Hutton),
    III, *l*; XXII, *k*; 26*, 69
    „   *laricinus* Sternberg, III, *k*;
        XXII, *i*; 26*, 69
Lepidophyllum acuminatum Lesquereux, IX, *l*
    „   *triangulare* Zeiller, IX, *j*;
        XXII, *d*; 31*, 32
Lepidostrobus brevifolius (Lesquereux), IX, *e*
    „   *hastatus* (Lesquereux), IX, *d*
    „   *incertus* (Lesquereux), IX, *i*
    „   *intermedius* (Lindley and Hut-
        ton), IX, *g*
    „   *lanceolatus* (Lindley and Hut-
        ton), IX, *f*; XXII, *c*; 32
    „   *majus* (Brongniart), IX, *k*
    „   *minus* (Goode), IX, *c*; XXII,
        a, *b*; 32
    „   *morissianus* (Lesquereux), IX, *h*
    „   *moyseyi* Arber, IX, *b*
    „   *olri* Zeiller, 26
    „   *radians* Schimper, IX, *a*
    „   *spinosus* Kidston, 32, 33
    „   *squarrosus* Kidston, 33
    „   *variabilis* Lindley and Hut-
        ton, 33
Linopteris münsteri (Eichwald), XVII, *b*;
    XXXI, *i*; 58
    „   *obliqua* (Bunbury), XVII, *d*;
        XXXVII, *c*; 58
Lonchopteris bricei Brongniart, XVI, *k*;
    XXIV, *g*; XXXVIII, *c*; 58
    „   *eschweileriana* Brongniart, XVI,
        l; XXIV, *h*; 58
    „   *rugosa* Brongniart, XVI, *j*;
        XXXVII, *d*; 58

Macrostachya infundibuliformis (Brongniart),
    XXV, *d*; 67
Margaritopteris convayi (Lindley and Hut-
    ton), XXXVII, *a*; 53
Mariopteris acuta (Brongniart), XV, *j*;
    XXXIX, *c*; 54
    „   *beneckei* Huth, XV, *k*; 54

Mariopteris hirta (Stur), XIV, *t*; XXXIX,
    d; 54
    „   *latifolia* (Brongniart), XV, *l*; 54
    „   *muricata* (Schlotheim), XIV, *r*;
        XXXIII, *g*; 54
    „   *nervosa* (Brongniart), XIV, *s*;
        XXXIII, *d*; 54*, 68, 69
    „   *sauveuri* (Brongniart), XXXIX,
        e; 54
Medullosa anglica Scott, 48, 63
Megaphyton frondosum Artis, XXXVIII, *a*;
    62
Muscites bertrandi Lignier, 17
    „   *polytrichaceus* Renault and Zeiller, 19

Neuropteris acuminata (Schlotheim), 59
    „   *auriculata* Brongniart, 60
    „   *blissi* Lesquereux, XVIII, *j*; 61
    „   *carpentieri* Kidston, XVIII, *l*; 61
    „   *crenulata* Brongniart, XVIII, *k*;
        61
    „   *dentata* Lesquereux, 59
    „   *diversifolia* Gothan and Jong-
        mans, 61
    „   *fimbriata* Lesquereux, XXVIII,
        b; 59*, 67
    „   *flexuosa* Sternberg, XVIII, *d*;
        XXVIII, *e*; 59*, 60, 67
    „   *gigantea* Sternberg, XVII, *e*;
        XXVIII, *f*; 59*, 60, 68
    „   *grangeri* Brongniart, XVIII, *f*;
        XXIII, *h*, *i*; 61*, 68
    „   *heterophylla* Brongniart, XVII, *c*;
        XXIX, *h*; 48, 58, 59, 60*, 61,
        63, 68, 69
    „   *kosmanni* Arber (? Potonié), 61
    „   *macrophylla* Brongniart, XVII, *i*;
        XXIX, *g*; 60*, 67
    „   *microphylla* Brongniart, XVIII,
        g; XXVIII, *i*; 60*, 68
    „   *obliqua* (Brongniart), XVII, *f*;
        XXIII, *j*; 48, 58*, 59, 60, 61,
        63, 68
    „   *obliqua* var. *impar* Weiss pro sp.,
        XXVIII, *a*; 59
    „   *osmundæ* (Artis), 60
    „   *ovata* Hoffmann, XVIII, *c*;
        XXVIII, *g*; 59*, 67
    „   *rarinervis* Bunbury, XVIII, *b*;
        XXV, *k*; 59, 60, 61*, 67, 68
    „   *rectinervis* Kidston, XVIII, *e*;
        XXIII, *k*; XXIX, *i*; 60*, 69
    „   *scheuchzeri* Hoffmann, XVII, *h*;
        XXVIII, *d*; 59*, 60, 67, 68
    „   *schlehani* Stur, XVIII, *a*;
        XXVIII, *c*; 59*, 60, 61
    „   *tenuifolia* (Schlotheim), XVII, *g*;
        XXVIII, *h*; 59, 60*, 68
    „   *villiersii* Brongniart, 60
Neuropterocarpus sp., XXXVI, *h*, 63

Sphenophyllum cf. *fasciculatum* Lesquereux, X, *h*; 37

„ cf. *longifolium* Germar, X, *i*; 37

„ *majus* (Bronn), X, *c*; XXIII, *f*; 36

„ *myriophyllum* Crépin, X, *e*, *f*; XXIII, *d*; 36

„ *oblongifolium* Germar and Kaulfuss, 37

„ *saxifragæfolium* (Sternberg), X, *d*; XXIII, *a*, *b*; 36*, 68, 69

„ *trichomatosum* Stur, X, *g*; XXIII, *e*; 36*, 68

„ *verticillatum* Zobel, 36

Sphenopteris alata Brongniart, XII,*j*; XXXII, *a*; 51*, 53, 67

„ *artemisæfolioides* Crépin, 51

„ *conwayi* Lindley and Hutton, 53

„ *dilatata* Lindley and Hutton, XII, *l*; XXXIII, *a*; 47, 51*, 68

„ *flabellifolia* Kidston, XIII, *j*; 53

„ *footneri* Marrat, XIII, *c*; 52

„ *hæninghausi* Brongniart, 53

„ *laurenti* Andrae, XII,*f*; XXXII, *d*; 50*, 68

„ *macilenta* Lindley and Hutton, XII, *c*; XXXII, *f*; 50*, 67

„ *neuropteroides* (Boulay), XII, *h*; XXXII, *e*; 17, 51*, 67

„ *nummularia* Gutbier, XIII,*f*; 53

„ *polyphylla* Lindley and Hutton, XIII, *h*; 53

„ *pseudofurcata* Kidston, XIII, *i*; 53

„ *sauveuri* Crépin, XII, *m*; XXXIII, *h*; 51*, 68

„ *schatzlarensis* (Stur), XII, *a*; XXV, *l*; 50*, 68

„ *schillingsi* Andrae, XIII, *g*; 53

„ *sewardi* Kidston, XIII, *l*; 54

Sphenopteris spiniformis Kidston, XII, *i*; XXXI, *f*; 51*, 68

„ *spinosa* Goeppert, 51

„ *stipulata* (Gutbier), XIII, *a*; 51

„ *striata* Gothan, XII, *e*; XXXII, *h*; 50, 51*, 53, 68, 69

„ *trifoliolata* (Artis), XII, *d*; XXXII, *g*; 50*, 51, 53, 68

„ *woodwardi* Kidston, XIII, *k*; 53

Spiropteris, XXVI, *g*; 62

Stachannularia calathifera Weiss, XXV, *g*

Stigmaria eveni Lesquereux, 34

„ *ficoides* (Sternberg), XXII, *f*; 33*, 34, 69

„ *minuta* Goeppert pro var., XXII, *e*; 33

„ *reticulata* Goeppert pro var., 34

Trigonocarpus dawesii Lindley and Hutton, 63

„ *næggerathi* (Sternberg), XXXVI, *i*; 63, 64*, 67

„ *oblongus* Lindley and Hutton, 63

„ *olivæformis* Lindley and Hutton, 63

„ *parkinsoni* Brongniart, XXXVI, *d*, *e*; 63*, 69

„ *shorensis* Salisbury, 63

Ulodendron minus Lindley and Hutton, XXI, *f*; 27, 29*

Urnatopteris herbacea (Boulay), 52

„ *tenella* (Brongniart), XII, *o*; XXXV, *e*; 52*, 69

Walchia hypnoides (Brongniart), 46

„ *imbricata* Schimper, XXXVI, *k*; 46*, 68

„ *piniformis* (Schlotheim), XXXVI, *l*; 46*, 68

GENERAL INDEX

COAL MEASURE PLANTS
PLATES I–XXXIX

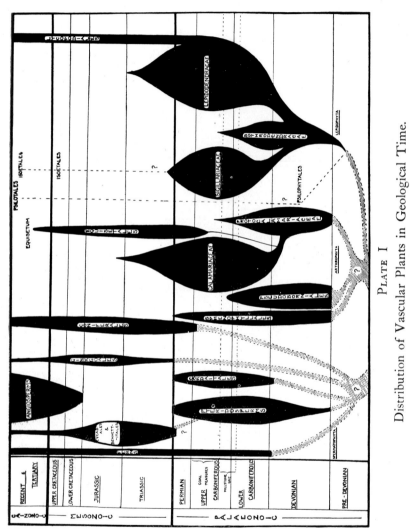

PLATE I

Distribution of Vascular Plants in Geological Time.

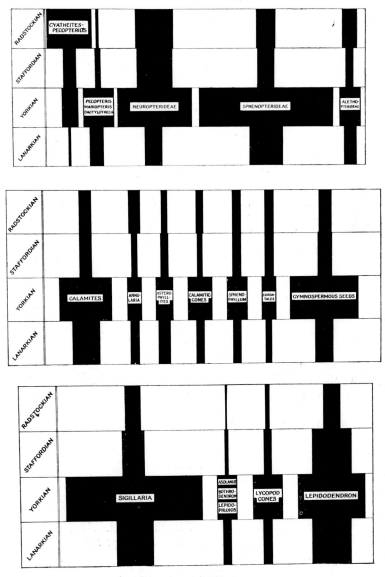

PLATE II

Diagrammatic Representation of the Relative Frequency with which
Various Groups of Plants occur as Incrustations in the Coal
Measures.

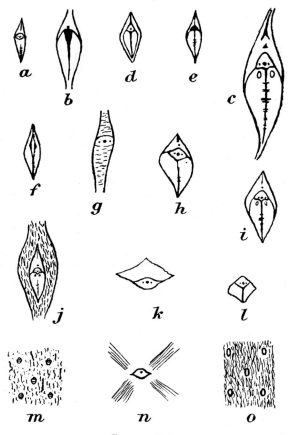

Leaf-cushions of *Lepidodendron*: a, *L. acutum*; b, *L. lanceolatum*; c, *L. aculeatum*; d, *L. ophiurus*; e, *L. simile*; f, *L. lycopodioides*; g, *L. wortheni*; h, *L. loricatum*; i, *L. obovatum*; j, *L. rimosum*. Leaf-cushions of *Lepidophloios*: k, *L. laricinus*; l, *L. acerosus*. Leaf-scars of *Bothrodendron*: m, *B. punctatum*; *Asolanus*: n, *A. camptetænia*; and *Pinakodendron*: o, *P. macconochiei*.

All figures approximately natural size.

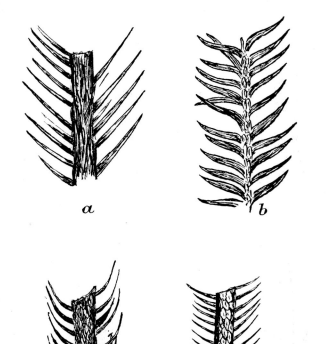

PLATE IV

Leafy twigs of *Lepidodendron*: a, *L. acutum*; b, *L. lanceolatum*; c, *L. ophiurus*; d, *L. simile*.

All figures approximately natural size.

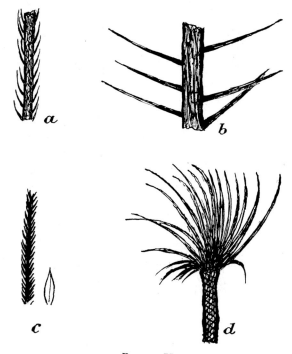

PLATE V

a, *Lepidodendron lycopodioides* Kidst.; b, *L. wortheni*; c, *Bothrodendron minutifolium*; d, *L. longifolium* Brongt.

All figures natural size.

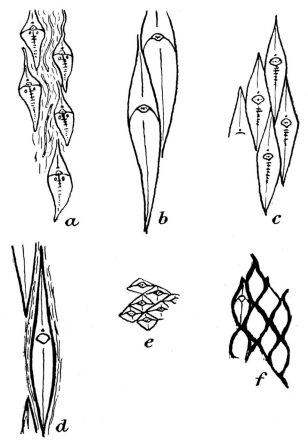

PLATE VI

Leaf-cushions of *Lepidodendron*: a, *L. distans*; b, *L. jaraczewski*; c, *L. fusiforme*; d, *L. gaudryi*; e, *L. peachi*; f, *L. landsburgi*.

All figures natural size.

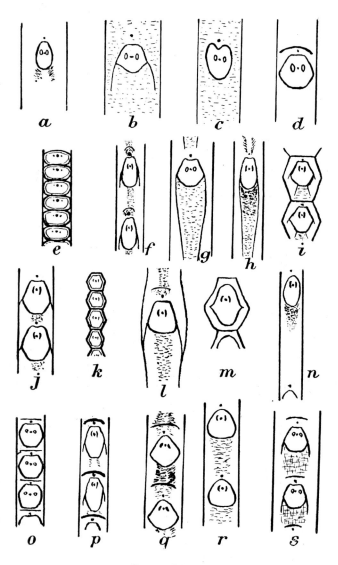

Plate VII

Leaf-scars of *Sigillaria*: a, *S. ovata*; b, *S. lævigata*; c, *S. cordigera*; d, *S. sauli*; e, *S. cumulata*; f, *S. elongata*; g, *S. deutschiana*; h, *S. rugosa*; i, j, *S. mammillaris*; k, *S. elegans*; l, *S. scutellata*; m, *S. trigona*; n, *S. candollei*; o, *S. tessellata*; p, *S. davreuxi*; q, *S. boblayi*; r, *S. essenia*; s, *S. principis*.

All figures approximately natural size.

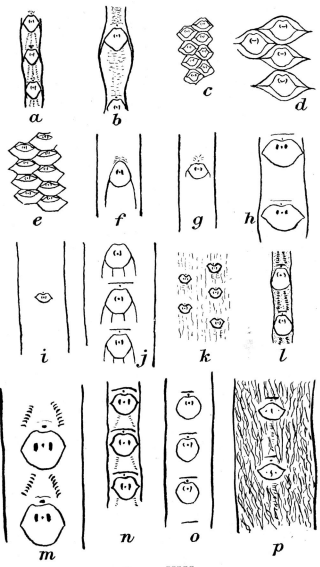

PLATE VIII

Leaf-scars of *Sigillaria*: a, *S. strivelensis*; b, *S. polyploca*; c, *S. incerta*; d, *S. brardi*; e, *S. semipulvinata*; f, *S. arzinensis*; g, *S. nudicaulis*; h, *S. transversalis*; i, *S. pringlei*; j, *S. reniformis*; k, *S. reticulata*; l, *S. punctirugosa*; m, *S. sol*; n, *S. micaudi*; o, *S. nortonensis*; p, *S. kidstoni.*

All figures natural size.

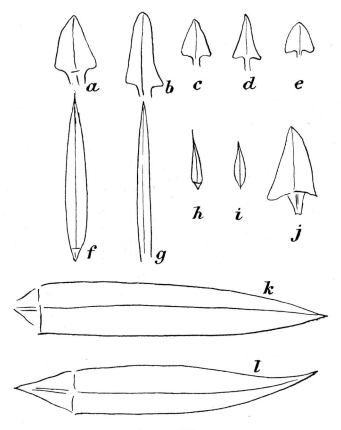

PLATE IX

Detached leaves of *Lepidophyllum* and sporophylls of *Lepidostrobus*: a, *L. radians* Schimper = *L. anthemis* (Koenig); b, *L. moyseyi* Arber; c, *L. minus* (Goode); d, *L. hastatus* (Lesqx.); e, *L. brevifolius* (Lesqx.); f, *L. lanceolatus* L. and H.; g, *L. intermedius* (L. and H.); h, *L morissianus* (Lesqx.); i, *L. incertus* (Lesqx.); j, *L. triangulare* Zeiller; k, *L. majus* (Brongt.); l, *L. acuminatum* Lesqx.

All figures natural size.

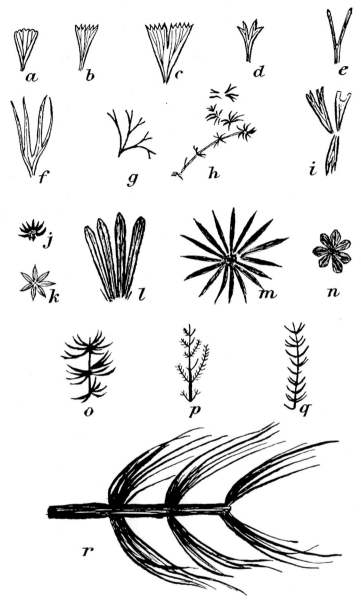

PLATE X

Leaves of *Sphenophyllum*: a, *S. emarginatum*; b, *S. cuneifolium*; c, *S. majus*;
d, *S. saxifragæfolium*; e, f, *S. myriophyllum*; g, *S. trichomatosum*;
h, *S.* cf. *fasciculatum*; i, *S.* cf. *longifolium*. Leaves of *Annularia*:
j, *A. microphylla*; k, *A. galioides*; l, *A. stellata*; m, *A. radiata*; n, *A. sphenophylloides*. Leafy twigs of *Asterophyllites*: o, *A. equisetiformis*;
p, *A. charæformis*; q, *A. grandis*; r, *A. longifolius*.

All figures natural size.

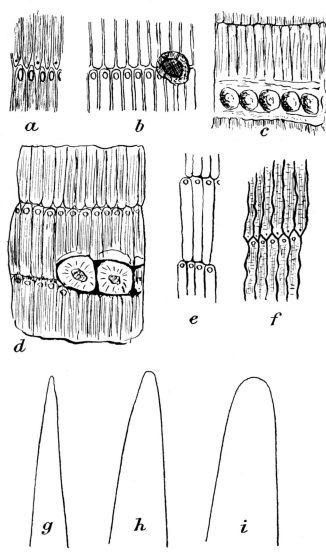

PLATE XI

Stems of *Calamites*: a, *C. cisti*; b, *C. carinatus*; c, *C. sachsei*; d, *C. goepperti*;
e, *C. suckowi*; f, *C. undulatus*.   Apices of leaves of Cordaites: g, *Dorycordaites palmæformis*; h, *Cordaites borassifolius*; i, *C. principalis*.

All figures natural size.

PLATE XII

Pinnules of Sphenopterideæ: a, *Sphenopteris schatzlarensis*; b, *Boweria schatzlarensis*; c, *S. macilenta*; d, *S. trifoliolata*; e, *S. striata*; f, *S. laurenti*; g, *Renaultia rotundifolia*; h, *S. neuropteroides*; i, *S. spiniformis*; j, *S. alata*; k, *Diplotmema furcatum*; l, *S. dilatata*; m, *S. sauveuri*; n, *Oligocarpia gutbieri*; o, *Urnatopteris tenella*; p, *Eremopteris artemisæfolia*; q, *Corynepteris coralloides*.

All figures approximately natural size.

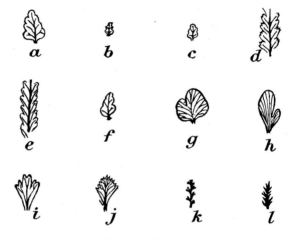

Pinnules of Sphenopterideæ: a, *S. stipulata*; b, *Renaultia gracilis*; c, *S. footneri*; d, *Alloiopteris serrula*; e, *A. radstockensis*; f, *S. nummularia*; g, *S. schillingsi*; h, *S. polyphylla*; i, *S. pseudofurcata*; j, *S. flabellifolia*; k, *S. woodwardi*; l, *S. sewardi*.

All figures natural size.

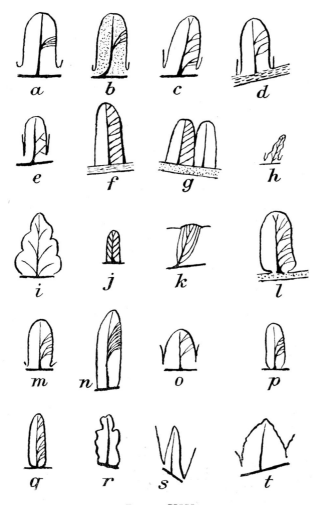

PLATE XIV

Pinnules of Pecoprideæ: a, *Acitheca polymorpha*; b, *Asterotheca abbreviata*; c, *A. oreopteridia*; d, *A. daubreei*; e, *A. crenulata*; f, *A. cyathea*; g, *A. arborescens*; h, *Dactylotheca plumosa*; i, *Dicksonites pluckeneti*; j, k, *Ptycho-carpus unitus*; l, *Eupecopteris fletti*; m, *E. cisti*; n, *E. pteroides*; o, *E. camertonensis*; p, *E. volkmanni*; q, *E. bucklandi*; r, *Mariopteris muricata*; s, *M. nervosa*; t, *M. hirta*.

All figures twice natural size.

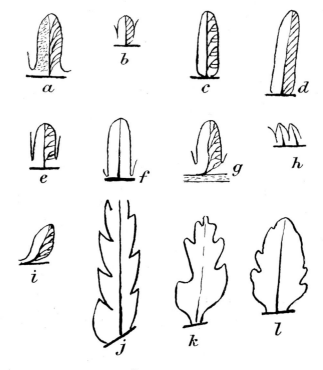

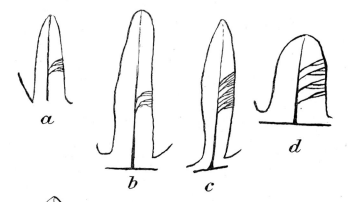

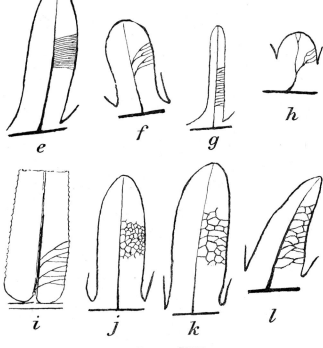

PLATE XVI

Pinnules of Alethopterideæ: a, *A. aquilina*; b, *A. davreuxi*; c, *A. lonchitica*; d, *A. valida*; e, *A. serli*; f, *A. grandini*; g, *A. decurrens*; h, *A. integra*; i, *Desmopteris longifolia*; j, *Lonchopteris rugosa*; k, *L. bricei*; l, *L. eschweileriana*.

All figures twice natural size.

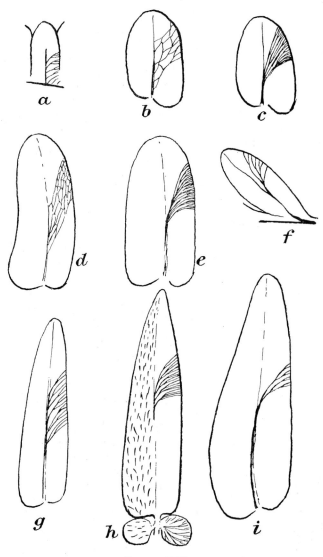

PLATE XVII

Pinnules of Neuropterideæ: a, *Callipteridium gigas*; b, *Linopteris münsteri*;
c, *Neuropteris heterophylla*; d, *Linopteris obliqua*; e, *Neuropteris gigantea*;
f, *N. obliqua*; g, *N. tenuifolia*; h, *N. scheuchzeri*; i, *N. macrophylla*.

With the exception of Fig. h (which is natural size), all figures twice natural size.

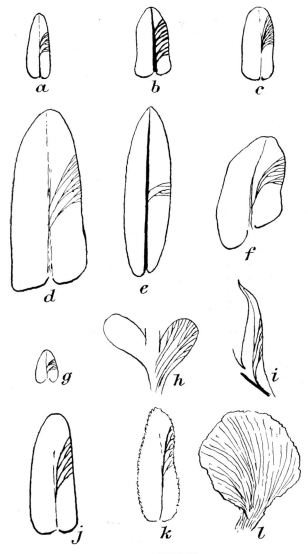

PLATE XVIII

Pinnules of Neuropterideæ: a, *N. schlehani*; b, *N. rarinervis*; c, *N. ovata*; d, *N. flexuosa*; e, *N. rectinervis*; f, *N. grangeri*; g, *N. microphylla*; h, *Odontopteris lindleyana*; i, *O. britannica*; j, *N. blissi*; k, *N. crenulata*; l, *N. carpentieri*.

All figures twice natural size.

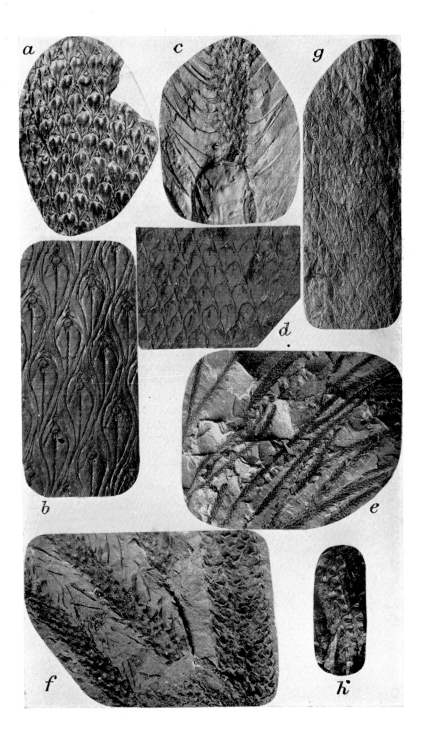

PLATE XXI

a. *Sigillaria rugosa* Brongt.   × 1.   (R.C.)
b. *Sigillaria tessellata* Brongt.   × 1.   (R.C.)
c. *Asolanus camptotænia* Wood.   × 1.   (R.C.)
d. *Sigillaria elegans* (Sternb.)   × 1.   (W.H.)
e. *Lepidodendron obovatum* Sternb.   × 1.   (R.K.)
f. *Sigillaria discophora* Koenig   × 1.   (R.K.)
g. *Sigillaria essenia* Achepohl   × 2.   (R.K.)

a

b

d

c

f

e

g

PLATE XXII

a, b. *Lepidostrobus minus* (Goode) × ½. (R.C.)
  c. *Lepidostrobus lanceolatus* (L. and H.) × ⅓. (R.C.)
  d. *Lepidphyllum triangulare* Zeiller × ½. (R.C.)
  e. *Stigmaria minuta* Goepp. pro var. × ½. (R.C.)
  f. *Stigmaria ficoides* (Sternb.) × ¼. (R.K.)
  g. *Sigillariostrobus rhombibracteatus* Kidst. × 6/7. (W.H.)
  h. *Bothrodendron minutifolium* (Boulay) × 1. (W.H.)
  i. *Lepidophloios laricinus* Sternb. × (about) 1/3. (R.K.)
  j. *Sigillaria lævigata* Brongt. × 1. (R.K.)
  k. *Lepidophloios acerosus* (L. and H.) × 1. (R.K.)

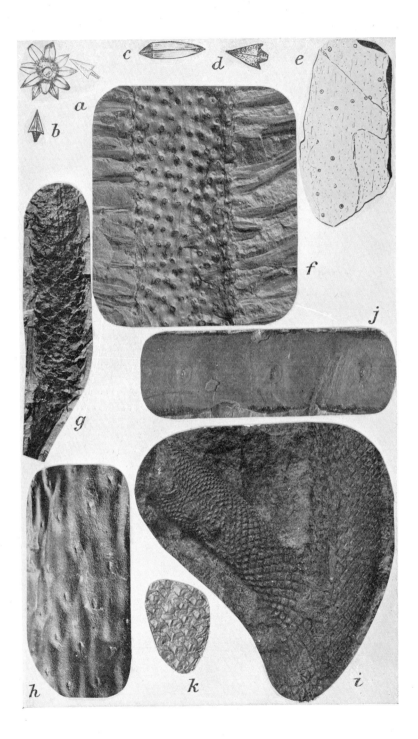

PLATE XXIII

a, b. *Sphenophyllum saxifragæfolium* (Sternb.)

    a. × ½. (R.C.)

    b. × 1. (W.H.)

c. *Sphenophyllum emarginatum* Brongt. × 1. (R.C.)

d. *Sphenophyllum myriophyllum* Crépin × 1. (R.C.)

e. *Sphenophyllum trichomatosum* Stur × 1. (R.C.)

f. *Sphenophyllum majus* (Bronn) × 1. (W.H.)

g. *Sphenophyllum cuneifolium* (Sternb.) × 4/3. (W.H.)

h. *Neuropteris grangeri* Brongt. × 2. (W.H.)

i. *Neuropteris grangeri* Brongt. × 1. (R.K.)

j. *Neuropteris obliqua* (Brongt.) × 2. (R.K.)

k. *Neuropteris rectinervis* Kidston × 1. (R.K.)

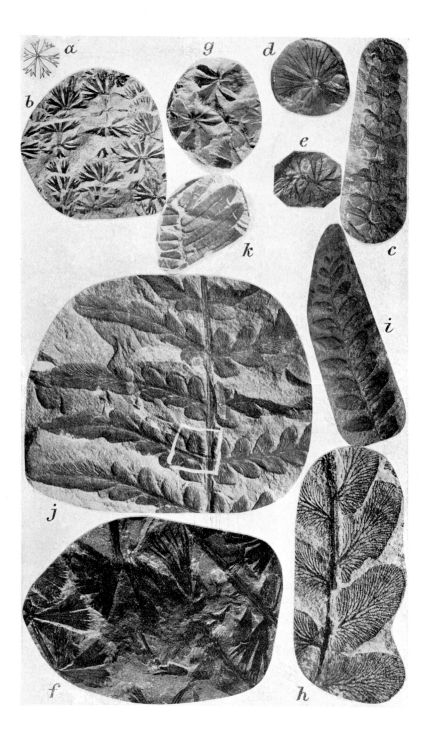

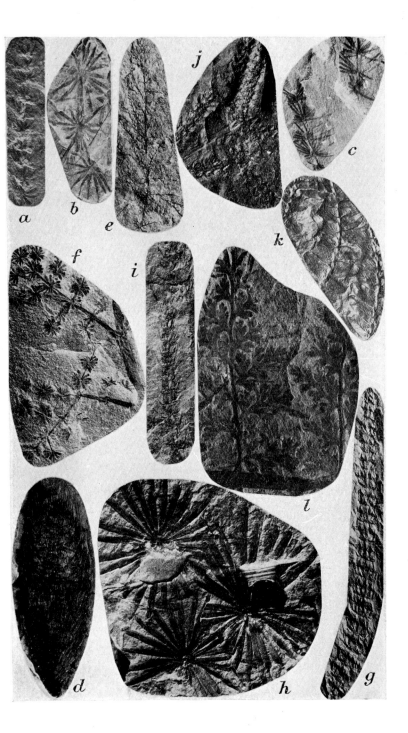

Plate XXVI

a. *Asterotheca arborescens* (Schloth.) × 1. (R.C.)
b. *Eupecopteris dentata* (Brongt.) × 1. (R.C.)
c. *Aphlebia linearis* (Gutb.) × ½. (W.H.)
d. *Asterotheca abbreviata* (Brongt.) × 1. (W.H.)
e. *Dactylotheca plumosa* (Artis) × 1. (W.H.)
f. *Acitheca polymorpha* (Brongt.) × 1. (R.K.)
g. *Spiropteris.* × 2. (R.K.)

PLATE XXVII

a. *Asterotheca crenulata* (Brongt.) × ½. (R.C.)
b. *Dicksonites pluckeneti* (Schloth.) × 1. (R.C.)
c. *Asterotheca cyathea* (Schloth.) × 1. (R.C.)
d. *Asterotheca daubreei* (Zeiller) × 1. (R.K.)
e. *Eupecopteris fletti* Kidston × 1. (R.K.)
f. *Eupecopteris bucklandi* (Brongt.) × 1. (R.K.)
g. *Asterotheca oreopteridia* (Schloth.) × 1. (R.K.)
h. *Eupecopteris cisti* (Brongt.) × 1. (R.K.)
i. *Ptychocarpus unitus* (Brongt.) × 1. (R.K.)

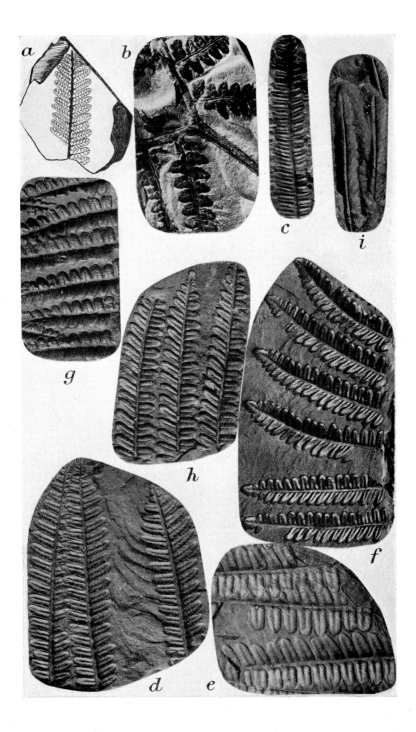

PLATE XXVIII

a. *Neuropteris obliqua* (Brongt.) forma *impar* Weiss pro sp.   × 1.   (R.K.)
b. *Neuropteris fimbriata* Lesqx.   × 1.   (R.C.)
c. *Neuropteris schlehani* Stur.   × $\frac{2}{3}$ (enlargement × 1).   (R.C.)
d. *Neuropteris scheuchzeri* Hoffm.   × 1.   (R.C.)
e. *Neuropteris flexuosa* Sternb.   × 1.   (R.C.)
f. *Neuropteris gigantea* Sternb.   × 1.   (R.C.)
g. *Neuropteris ovata* Hoffm.   × 1.   (R.C.)
h. *Neuropteris tenuifolia* (Schloth.)   × 1.   (R.K.)
i. *Neuropteris microphylla* Brongt.   × 1.   (R.K.)

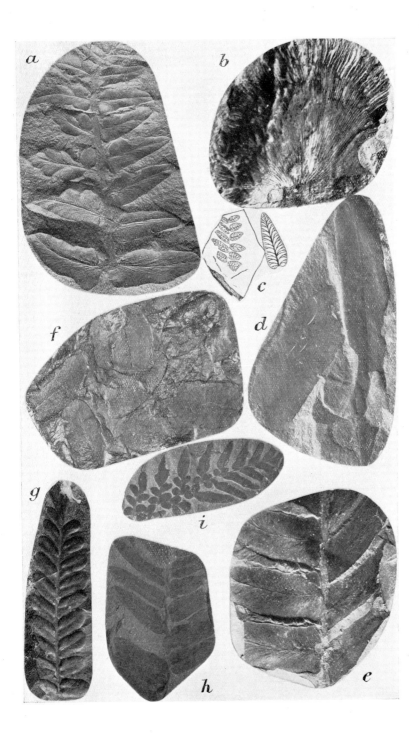

PLATE **XXIX**

a. *Cyclopteris reniformis* Brongt. $\times$ 1. (R.K.)
b. *Cyclopteris orbicularis* Brongt. $\times$ 1. (R.C.)
c. *Cyclopteris sp.* $\times$ ½. (R.C.)
d. *Aphlebia spinosa* Lesqx. $\times$ 1. (R.C.)
e. *Odontopteris lindleyana* Sternb. $\times$ 2. (R.K.)
f. *Odontopteris britannica* Gutb. $\times$ 2. (R.K.)
g. *Neuropteris macrophylla* Brongt. $\times$ 1. (R.C.)
h. *Neuropteris heterophylla* Brongt. $\times$ 1. (W.H.)
i. *Neuropteris rectinervis* Kidst. $\times$ 2. (R.K.)

a

c

b

d

f

g

e

h

PLATE XXXI

a. *Eupecopteris camertonensis* Kidst.   × 1.   (R.K.)
b. *Eupecopteris volkmanni* (Sauveur)   × 1.   (R.K.)
c, d. *Callipteridium gigas* (Gutb.)
      c. × 1.   (R.K.)
      d. × 3.   (R.K.)
e. *Crossotheca pinnatafida* (Gutb.)   × 1.   (R.K.)
f. *Sphenopteris spiniformis* Kidst.   × 1.   (R.K.)
g. *Corynepteris coralloides* (Gutb.)   × 2.   (R.K.)
h. *Renaultia gracilis* (Brongt.)   × 2.   (R.K.)
i. *Linopteris münsteri* (Eichwald)   × 1.   (R.K.)

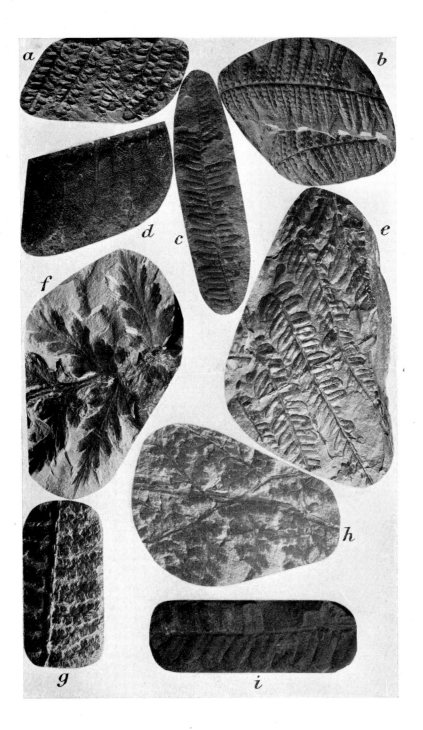

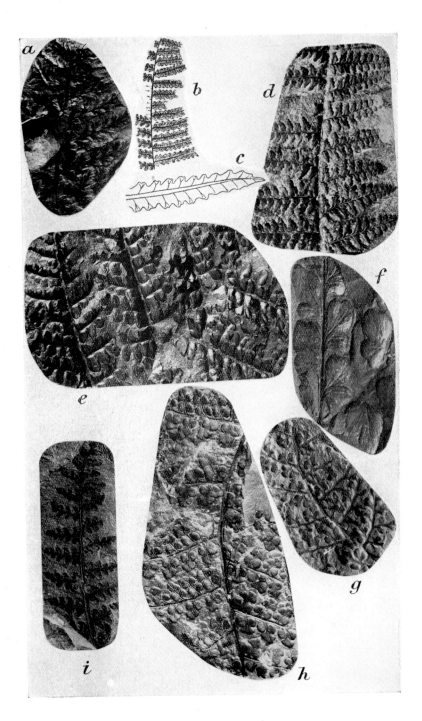

PLATE XXXIV

a. *Cordaites angulosostriatus* Grand 'Eury   × 4/5.   (R.C.)
b. *Poacordaites microstachys* (Gold.)   × 1.   (R.C.)
c. *Cordaites principalis* (Germar)   × 1.   (R.C.)
d. *Cordaites borassifolius* (Sternb.)   × ½.   (W.H.)
e. *Cordaianthus volkmanni* (Ett.)   × 2.   (W.H.)
f. *Dorycordaites palmæformis* (Goeppert)   × 3/5.   (W.H.)
g. *Cordaianthus pitcairniæ* (L. and H.)   × 1.   (W.H.)
h. *Renaultia gracilis* (Brongt.)   × 1.   (R.K.)
i. *Oligocarpia gutbieri* Goeppert   × 1.   (R.K.)

PLATE XXXVI

a. *Caulopteris anglica* Kidst. × 4/5. (R.C.)
b. *Holcospermum mammillatum* (Lesqx.) × 1. (R.C.)
c. *Carpolithus inflatus* (Lesqx.) × 1. (R.C.)
d, e. *Trigonocarpus parkinsoni* Brongt. × $\frac{2}{3}$. (R.C.)
f. *Carpolithus areolatus* (Boulay) × 1. (R.C.)
g. *Cordaicarpus crassus* (Lesqx.) × 1. (R.K.)
h. *Neuropterocarpus sp.* × 1. (R.K.)
i. *Trigonocarpus nœggerathi* (Sternb.) × $\frac{1}{2}$. (R.C.)
j. *Holcospermum elongatum* (Kidst.) × 1. (W.H.)
k. *Walchia imbricata* Schimper × 1. (R.K.)
l. *Walchia piniformis* (Schloth.) × $\frac{1}{2}$. (R.K.)
m. *Samaropsis acuta* (L. and H.) × 1. (R.K.)
n. *Alethopteris valida* Boulay × 1. (R.K.)

b

                                                                        c

e   d

A SELECTION OF
Messrs. Edward Arnold & Co.'s
Scientific & Technical Publications

PHYSICS

GENERAL ASTRONOMY. By H. Spencer Jones, M.A., Sc.D., H.M. Astronomer at the Cape. viii + 392 pages, with 102 diagrams and 24 plates. Third Impression. Demy 8vo, 21s. net.

THE LIFE OF LORD RAYLEIGH. By his son, Robert John Strutt, Fourth Baron Rayleigh, F.R.S. Demy 8vo, xii + 403 pages. 25s. net.

ISOTOPES. By F. W. Aston, Sc.D., D.Sc., F.R.S., Nobel Laureate, Fellow of Trinity College, Cambridge. viii + 182 pages, with diagrams and plates. Second Edition. Demy 8vo, 10s. 6d. net.

IONS, ELECTRONS, AND IONIZING RADIATIONS. By J. A. Crowther, M.A., Sc.D., Professor of Physics at the University of Reading. Fifth Edition. Thoroughly revised. xii + 353 pages. Demy 8vo, 12s. 6d. net.

THE DYNAMICAL THEORY OF SOUND. By Horace Lamb, Sc.D., F.R.S., Rayleigh Lecturer in the University of Cambridge. Second Edition. viii + 307 pages. Demy 8vo, 18s. net.

SOUND. A Physical Textbook. By E. G. Richardson, M.Sc., Ph.D., Assistant Lecturer in the Physics Department, University College, London. viii + 286 pages, with 86 illustrations. Demy 8vo, 15s. net.

THE ACOUSTICS OF ORCHESTRAL INSTRUMENTS AND OF THE ORGAN. By E. G. Richardson, M.Sc., Ph.D. Demy 8vo, 160 pages, with 20 plates. 10s. 6d. net.

AN INTRODUCTION TO THE THEORY OF OPTICS. By Sir Arthur Schuster, Sc.D., F.R.S. Third Edition. Revised by the Author and J. W. Nicholson, D.Sc., F.R.S., Fellow and Tutor of Balliol College, Oxford. xvi + 405 pages, 188 illustrations. Demy 8vo, 18s. net.

COLOUR VISION. A Discussion of the Leading Phenomena and their Physical Laws. By W. Peddie, D.Sc., F.R.S.E., Harris Professor of Physics at University College, Dundee. xii + 208 pages. Demy 8vo, 12s. 6d. net.

MOLECULAR MAGNETISM. By W. Peddie, D.Sc., F.R.S.E. Demy 8vo. 160 pages.

AERONAUTICS IN THEORY AND EXPERIMENT. By W. L. Cowley, A.R.C.S., D.I.C., and H. Levy, M.A., D.Sc., F.R.S.E. Second Edition. xii + 332 pages. Demy 8vo, 25s. net.

A TEXT-BOOK OF PHYSICS. By R. S. Willows, M.A. (Camb.), D.Sc. (London). Third Edition. viii + 520 pages, with 320 diagrams. Large crown 8vo, 9s.

THE PRINCIPLES OF PHYSICS. A Textbook for Students of Pharmacy. By C. J. Smith, Ph.D., D.I.C. Crown 8vo. viii + 288. pages 9s.

AN INTRODUCTION TO FLUID MOTION. By W. N. Bond, D.Sc., F.Inst.P., Lecturer in Physics at the University of Reading. Crown 8vo. 5s. net.

HEAT. By W. J. R. Calvert, M.A., Harrow School. viii + 344 pages, with 138 diagrams. Crown 8vo, 6s.

LIGHT. By F. BRAY, M.A., late Science Master at Clifton College. xvi + 284 pages, with 234 diagrams and 6 plates. Crown 8vo, cloth, 6s.

ELECTRICITY AND MAGNETISM. By C. E. ASHFORD, M.A., Headmaster of the Royal Naval College, Dartmouth. With over 200 diagrams. THIRD REVISED EDITION. Crown 8vo, 4s. 6d.

ADVANCED EXAMPLES IN PHYSICS. By A. O. ALLEN, M.A., B.Sc., A.R.C.S., Lecturer in Optics at Leeds University. SECOND EDITION. Crown 8vo, 2s. 6d. net.

MATHEMATICS

FIVE-FIGURE TABLES OF MATHEMATICAL FUNCTIONS. By J. B. DALE, M.A., Assistant Professor of Mathematics at King's College, London. Demy 8vo, 4s. 6d. net.

LOGARITHMIC AND TRIGONOMETRIC TABLES (To Five Places of Decimals). By J. B. DALE, M.A. Demy 8vo, 2s. 6d. net.

THE CALCULUS FOR ENGINEERS. By JOHN PERRY, M.E., D.Sc., F.R.S. THIRTEENTH IMPRESSION. viii + 382 pages. Crown 8vo, 8s. 6d.

CALCULUS FOR TECHNICAL STUDENTS. By S. N. FORREST, M.A., B.Sc. Crown 8vo, viii + 231 pages, 5s.

CALCULUS FOR SCHOOLS. By R. C. FAWDRY, M.A., Head of the Military and Engineering Side at Clifton College ; and C. V. DURELL, Senior Mathematical Master at Winchester College. Crown 8vo. With Answers. In one volume, 6s. 6d. Part I, 3s. 6d.; Part II, 4s.

AN INTRODUCTION TO PROJECTIVE GEOMETRY. By L. N. G. FILON, M.A., D.Sc., F.R.S., Professor of Applied Mechanics, University College, University of London. THIRD EDITION. viii + 261 pages. Crown 8vo, 7s. 6d.

HIGHER ALGEBRA. By W. P. MILNE, M.A., D.Sc., Professor of Mathematics in the University of Leeds. xii + 586 pages. Crown 8vo, 8s. 6d.

HOMOGENEOUS CO-ORDINATES. By W. P. MILNE, M.A., D.Sc. xii + 164 pages. Crown 8vo, 6s. net.

ENGINEERING

BRITISH ENGINEERING WAGES. By R. SPICER. Demy 8vo. 160 pages. 10s. 6d. net.

THE STRENGTH OF MATERIALS. A Treatise on the Theory of Stress Calculations for Engineers. By J. CASE, M.A., F.R.Ae.S., Lecturer in Applied Mechanics at the Royal Naval Engineering College, Keyham. Med. 8vo. viii + 558 pages. 30s. net.

STRENGTH AND STRUCTURE OF STEEL AND OTHER METALS. By W. E. DALBY, F.R.S., M.A., B.Sc., M.Inst.C.E., M.I.M.E., University Professor of Engineering at the City and Guilds (Engineering) College. Very fully illustrated. 192 pages and 38 plates. 8vo, 18s. net.

STEAM POWER. By Professor W. E. DALBY, F.R.S., M.Inst.C.E., M.I.M.E. SECOND EDITION. xvi + 760 pages, with 250 diagrams. 8vo, 25s. net.

VALVES AND VALVE GEAR MECHANISMS. By Professor W. E. DALBY, F.R.S. xviii + 366 pages, 202 illustrations. Royal 8vo, 24s. net.

THE BALANCING OF ENGINES. By Professor W. E. DALBY, F.R.S. THIRD EDITION. xii + 283 pages, 184 illustrations. Demy 8vo, 12s. 6d. net.

PROPERTIES OF STEAM AND THERMODYNAMIC THEORY OF TURBINES. By H. L. CALLENDAR, F.R.S., Professor of Physics in the Imperial College of Science and Technology. 544 pages, numerous diagrams. 8vo, 30s. net.

LONDON : EDWARD ARNOLD & CO., 41 & 43 MADDOX ST., W.1.

THE ENLARGED CALLENDAR STEAM TABLES. (Fahrenheit Units.) 7s. 6d. net.

THE CALLENDAR STEAM TABLES. 3s. 6d. net.

ABRIDGED CALLENDAR STEAM TABLES. (Centigrade Units.) SECOND EDITION. 8vo, 1s. net.

ABRIDGED CALLENDAR STEAM TABLES. (Fahrenheit Units.) SECOND EDITION. 8vo, 1s. net.

THE MOLLIER DIAGRAM. Drawn by Professor CALLENDAR and printed on green squared paper. 1s. net.

THE ENLARGED MOLLIER DIAGRAM. Drawn by Professor CALLENDAR. Printed in three colours on squared paper. 4s. net.

THE CALLENDAR STEAM DIAGRAM. (Centigrade Units.) 6d. net.

THE CALLENDAR STEAM DIAGRAM. (Fahrenheit Units.) 6d. net.

HEAT DROP TABLES: ABSOLUTE PRESSURES. Calculated by H. Moss, M.Sc., A.R.C.S., from the Formulæ and Steam Tables of Professor H. L. Callendar, F.R.S. 64 pages. Cloth, 5s. net.

HEAT DROP TABLES: H.P. GAUGE PRESSURES, L.P. ABSO-LUTE PRESSURES. Calculated by H. Moss, Imperial College of Science, from Professor Callendar's Formulæ and Steam Tables. Cloth, 5s. net.

THE ENLARGED HEAT DROP TABLES: H.P. GAUGE PRES-SURES, L.P. ABSOLUTE PRESSURES. 10s. 6d. net.

CORRECTION TABLES FOR THERMODYNAMIC EFFICIENCY. Calculated by C. H. NAYLOR, Assoc.M.Inst.C.E. Cloth, 5s. net.

ELECTRICAL SUBSTATIONS. By H. BRAZIL, M.I.E.E. 224 pages, with 56 illustrations. Demy 8vo, 12s. 6d. net.

RAILWAY ELECTRIC TRACTION. By F. W. CARTER, Sc.D., M.I.E.E., M.Inst.C.E., British Thomson-Houston Co., Rugby. viii + 412 pages, with 204 illustrations and 10 folding plates. Demy 8vo, 25s. net.

ELECTRIC TRAINS. By R. E. DICKINSON, B.Sc., A.M.I.E.E. xii + 292 pages, with 139 diagrams. Demy 8vo, 16s. net.

THE PRACTICE OF RAILWAY SURVEYING AND PERMANENT WAY WORK. By S. WRIGHT PERROTT, M.A.I., M.Inst.C.E., and F. E. G. BADGER, A.M.Inst.C.E. viii + 304 pages, with 140 diagrams. Demy 8vo, 30s. net.

THE ECONOMICS OF RAIL TRANSPORT IN GREAT BRITAIN. By C. E. R. SHERRINGTON, M.A., A.M.Inst.T., London School of Economics. Vol. I, History and Development. Vol. II, Rates and Service. Demy 8vo, 12s. 6d. net each volume.

THE MEASUREMENT OF FLUID VELOCITY AND PRESSURE. By the late J. R. PANNELL. Edited by R. A. FRAZER, B.A., B.Sc., National Physical Laboratory. viii + 138 pages. 10s. 6d. net.

HYDRAULICS. For Engineers and Engineering Students. By F. C. LEA, D.Sc., M.Inst.C.E., Professor of Mechanical Engineering in the University of Sheffield. FOURTH EDITION. xii + 594 pages, 400 diagrams. Demy 8vo, 18s. net.

ELEMENTARY HYDRAULICS. For Technical Students. By F. C. LEA, D.Sc., M.Inst.C.E. viii + 224 pages, with 156 diagrams. Crown 8vo, 7s. 6d.

MODERN METHODS OF WATER PURIFICATION. By JOHN DON, F.I.C., A.M.I.Mech.E., and JOHN CHISHOLM, A.M.I.Mech.E. SECOND EDITION. xviii + 398 pages, 106 illustrations. Demy 8vo, 16s. net.

REINFORCED CONCRETE DESIGN. VOL. I.: THEORY. By OSCAR FABER, D.Sc., M.Inst.C.E., and P. G. BOWIE, A.M.Inst.C.E. xx + 332 pages, 158 diagrams. SECOND EDITION. Demy 8vo, 14s. net. VOL. II.: PRACTICE. By OSCAR FABER, D.Sc., M.Inst.C.E. xii + 246 pages, 89 diagrams. Demy 8vo, 18s. net.

LONDON: EDWARD ARNOLD & CO., 41 & 43 MADDOX ST., W.1.

MODERN ROADS. By H. P. Boulnois, M.Inst.C.E., F.R.San.Inst., etc.
xii + 302 pages. Demy 8vo, 16s. net.

SURVEYING. By W. N. Thomas, M.Sc. (Birmingham), B.Sc. Eng.
(London), Assoc.M.Inst.C.E., A.M.I.Mech.E., A.M.Inst. M. and Cy.E. Second
Edition. viii + 536 pages and 298 diagrams. 8vo, 25s. net.

THE FIELD ENGINEER'S HANDBOOK. By G. C. Wells and
A. S. Clay, B.Sc. Second Edition. Small 8vo, 8s. 6d. net.

TRAVERSE TABLES. By Henry Louis, M.A., D.Sc., M.I.C.E., and
G. W. Caunt, M.A. Second Edition. 8vo, 5s. 6d. net.

TACHEOMETER TABLES. By H. Louis, M.A., D.Sc., M.I.C.E., and
G. W. Caunt, M.A. 8vo, 10s. 6d. net.

A TEXT-BOOK OF ELECTRICAL ENGINEERING. By Dr. A.
Thomälen. Translated by Professor G. W. O. Howe, D.Sc. Fourth Edition.
xii + 482 pages, 480 diagrams. Demy 8vo, 28s. net.

**THE PRINCIPLES OF ELECTRICAL ENGINEERING AND THEIR
APPLICATION.** By Dr. G. Kapp. Volume I.: Principles. xii + 356
pages. Demy 8vo, 18s. net. Volume II.: Application. x + 388 pages. 18s. net.

THE THEORY OF MACHINES. By R. F. McKay, M.Sc., A.M.Inst.
C.E. Second Edition. viii + 440 pages, 407 diagrams. Demy 8vo, 20s. net.

GRINDING MACHINERY. By J. J. Guest, M.A., M.I.Mech.E. xii
+ 444 pages, with illustrations. Demy 8vo, 16s. net.

METAL WORK. By H. M. Adam and J. H. Evans. Second Edition.
277 pages, with 217 illustrations. Crown 8vo. Cloth, 6s. 6d.

**THE STRENGTH AND ELASTICITY OF STRUCTURAL MEM-
BERS.** By R. J. Woods, M.E., M.Inst.C.E. Second Edition. xii + 310
pages, 292 illustrations. Demy 8vo, 14s. net.

**EXAMPLES IN THE STRENGTH AND ELASTICITY OF
MATERIALS.** By G. W. Bird, B.Sc. Crown 8vo. 10s. 6d.

THE THEORY OF STRUCTURES. By R. J. Woods, M.E., M.Inst.
C.E. xii + 276 pages, 157 illustrations. Demy 8vo, 12s. 6d. net.

THE ITALIAN ORDERS OF ARCHITECTURE. By Charles
Gourlay, B.Sc., A.R.I.B.A. With 32 full-page plates. Large 4to (12″ × 9½″).
Second Edition. 8s. net.

AN INTRODUCTION TO BUILDING SCIENCE. By F. L. Brady,
M.Sc., A.I.C. Crown 8vo, viii + 280 pages, with 63 illustrations. 7s. 6d.

**MECHANICAL DRAWING. With Special Reference to the Needs
of Mining Students.** By Joseph Husband, B.Eng., A.M.I.C.E., Professor
of Civil Engineering at Sheffield University. With 40 plates. Quarto, 3s. 6d.

MACHINE SKETCHES AND DESIGNS. By Professor A. Cruick-
shank, M.I.Mech.E., and R. F. McKay, M.Sc., A.M.Inst.C.E. Third Edition.
Quarto, 2s. 6d.

FIRST YEAR ELECTRICAL ENGINEERING. By D. J. Bolton,
M.Sc., M.I.E.E., Lecturer at the Polytechnic, London. Crown 8vo.

EXAMPLES IN ELECTRICAL ENGINEERING. By Professor J. F.
Gill, M.Sc., B.Eng., A.M.I.Mech.E.; and F. J. Teago, D.Sc., M.I.E.E., The University, Liverpool. Second Edition. Crown 8vo, 7s. 6d. net.

LONDON : EDWARD ARNOLD & CO., 41 & 43 MADDOX ST., W.1.

GEOLOGY AND MINING

THE GEOLOGY OF THE BRITISH EMPIRE. By F. R. C. REED, Sc.D., F.G.S. viii + 480 pages, with 25 maps and sections. Demy 8vo, 30s. net.

THE STRUCTURE OF THE ALPS. By L. W. COLLET, D.Sc. xii + 282 pages, with 63 figures and 12 plates. Demy 8vo, 16s. net.

STRUCTURE AND SURFACE. A Book of Field Geology. By C. BARRINGTON BROWN, M.A., F.G.S., [and F. DEBENHAM, M.A., F.G.S. viii + 168 pages, with 104 illustrations. Medium 8vo, 10s. 6d. net.

PHYSICO-CHEMICAL GEOLOGY. By R. H. RASTALL, Sc.D., Lecturer in Economic Geology in the University of Cambridge. viii + 48 pages, with 62 diagrams. 15s. net.

OIL FINDING : An Introduction to the Geological Study of Petroleum. By E. H. CUNNINGHAM CRAIG, B.A., F.G.S. SECOND EDITION. xii + 324 pages, 13 plates and 20 illustrations. Demy 8vo, cloth, 16s. net.

THE DRESSING OF MINERALS. By H. LOUIS, D.Sc., M.I.M.E., M.Inst.C.E. x + 544 pages, 416 illustrations. Super royal 8vo, cloth, 30s. net.

COAL IN GREAT BRITAIN. By WALCOT GIBSON, D.Sc., F.G.S., F.R.S.E. SECOND EDITION. viii + 312 pages, with 50 diagrams and 8 plates. Demy 8vo, 21s. net.

COAL MEASURE PLANTS. By R. CROOKALL, Ph.D., of the Geological Survey of Great Britain. Demy 8vo, with 40 plates. 12s. 6d. net.

THE ECONOMICS OF COAL MINING. By R. W. DRON, M.A., F.R.S.E., Professor of Mining in the University of Glasgow. viii + 168 pages, with 13 figures and 26 tables. Demy 8vo, 10s. 6d. net.

MINING SUBSIDENCE. By HENRY BRIGGS, C.B.E., D.Sc., Professor of Mining in the University of Edinburgh. Demy 8vo. viii + 216 pages. 14s. net.

WINDING ENGINES AND WINDING APPLIANCES : Their Design and Economical Working. By G. McCULLOCH, A.M.I.M.E., and T. C. FUTERS, M.Inst.M.E. viii + 452 pages, 175 illustrations. Demy 8vo, 21s. net.

A TEXTBOOK OF GEOLOGY. By P. LAKE, M.A., F.G.S., and R. H. RASTALL, Sc.D., F.G.S. xiv + 508 pages, fully illustrated. FOURTH EDITION. Demy 8vo, 21s. net.

OUTLINES OF PALÆONTOLOGY. By H. H. SWINNERTON, D.Sc., F.G.S. xii + 420 pages, with 368 diagrams. Demy 8vo, cloth, 30s. net.

THE PHYSIOGRAPHICAL EVOLUTION OF BRITAIN. By L. J. WILLS, Sc.D., F.G.S., Lecturer in Geology in the University of Birmingham. Demy 8vo.

THE GEOLOGY OF ORE DEPOSITS. By H. H. THOMAS, M.A., B.Sc., and D. A. MACALISTER, A.R.S.M. Crown 8vo, 8s. 6d. net.

THE GEOLOGY OF BUILDING STONES. By J. ALLEN HOWE, B.Sc. viii + 455 pages, fully illustrated. Crown 8vo, 8s. 6d. net.

THE GEOLOGY OF SOILS AND SUBSTRATA. By the late H. B. WOODWARD, F.R.S. xvi + 366 pages, with illustrations. Crown 8vo, 8s. 6d. net.

GEOLOGICAL AND TOPOGRAPHICAL MAPS : Their Interpretation and Use. By A. R. DWERRYHOUSE, D.Sc., F.G.S. SECOND EDITION. viii + 133 pages, with 90 illustrations. Demy 8vo, 6s. net.

AN INTRODUCTION TO MINE SURVEYING. By T. BRYSON, A.R.T.C., M.I.Min.E., and G. M. CHAMBERS, M.Inst.M.E. 6s.

THEORY AND PRACTICE OF MINE VENTILATION. By T. BRYSON, M.I.Min.E. viii + 255 pages, with 81 illustrations. Crown 8vo., 8s. 6d.

LONDON : EDWARD ARNOLD & CO., 41 & 43 MADDOX ST., W.1.

CHEMISTRY AND METALLURGY

THE DISCOVERY OF THE RARE GASES. By MORRIS W. TRAVERS, D.Sc., F.R.S. viii + 128 pages, with facsimile reproductions from Sir William Ramsay's Notebooks. Demy 4to, 15s. net.

THE ORDINALL OF ALCHIMY. Written by THOMAS NORTON of Bristoll. Facsimile Reproduction from *Theatrum Chemicum Britannicum.* viii + 125 pages. Demy 8vo, 10s. 6d. net.

AN ETYMOLOGICAL DICTIONARY OF CHEMISTRY AND MINERALOGY. By DOROTHY BAILEY, B.Sc., Ph.D., and KENNETH C. BAILEY, M.A., Sc.D. xii + 292 pages. Demy 8vo, 25s. net.

THE ELDER PLINY'S CHAPTERS ON CHEMICAL SUBJECTS. Translated with a critical commentary by KENNETH C. BAILEY, M.A., Sc.D. Demy 8vo, 12s. 6d. net.

METALS AND METALLIC COMPOUNDS. By U. R. EVANS, M.A., King's College, Cambridge. 4 vols., obtainable separately. Demy 8vo. Vol. I., 21s. net. Vol. II., 18s. net. Vol. III., 14s. net. Vol. IV., 18s. net.

THE CORROSION OF METALS. By U. R. EVANS, M.A. SECOND EDITION. Demy 8vo. xvi + 259 pages. 15s. net.

A BIBLIOGRAPHY OF METALLIC CORROSION. By W. H. J. VERNON, D.Sc., F.I.C. xii + 341 pages. Demy 8vo, 21s. net.

SERVICE CHEMISTRY. By the late VIVIAN B. LEWES, F.I.C., F.C.S. ; and J. S. S. BRAME, F.I.C., F.C.S., Professor of Chemistry, Royal Naval College, Greenwich. FIFTH EDITION. xvi + 576 pages. Illustrated. Demy 8vo, 21s.

FUEL. Solid, Liquid, and Gaseous. By J. S. S. BRAME, F.I.C. THIRD EDITION. xvi + 388 pages, 73 diagrams. Demy 8vo, 18s. net.

PETROL AND PETROLEUM SPIRITS. A Description of their Sources, Preparation, Examination, and Uses. By W. E. GOODAY, A.R.S.M., D.I.C., A.M.Inst.P.T. xii + 135 pages. Demy 8vo, 10s. 6d. net.

THE ABSORPTION OF NITROUS GASES. By H. W. WEBB, M.Sc., F.I.C. Demy 8vo, 25s. net.

THE RARE EARTHS : Their Occurrence, Chemistry and Technology. By S. I. LEVY, M.A., F.I.C. xvi + 362 pages. Demy 8vo, 18s. net.

THE CHEMISTRY AND MANUFACTURE OF HYDROGEN. By P. LITHERLAND TEED, A.R.S.M. Illustrated. Demy 8vo, cloth, 10s. 6d. net.

THE PRINCIPLES OF APPLIED ELECTRO-CHEMISTRY. By A. J. ALLMAND, D.Sc., Professor of Chemistry, King's College, London, and H. J. T. ELLINGHAM, B.Sc. SECOND EDITION. Medium 8vo. xii + 727 pages and 171 diagrams. 35s. net.

ANTIQUES : Their Restoration and Preservation. By A. LUCAS, F.I.C. Crown 8vo, 6s. net.

ANCIENT EGYPTIAN MATERIALS. By A. LUCAS, F.I.C. Crown 8vo, 7s. 6d. net.

FORENSIC CHEMISTRY. By A. LUCAS, O.B.E., F.I.C. viii + 268 pages. Demy 8vo, 15s. net.

OUTLINES OF ORGANIC CHEMISTRY. By E. J. HOLMYARD, M.A., F.I.C. viii + 456 pages. Crown 8vo, 7s. 6d.

ORGANIC CHEMISTRY FOR ADVANCED STUDENTS. By JULIUS B. COHEN, Ph.D., D.Sc., F.R.S. FIFTH EDITION, in Three Parts, obtainable separately. Demy 8vo, 18s. net each part.

THE CONSTITUTION OF SUGARS. By W. N. HAWORTH, D.Sc., F.R.S., Professor of Chemistry in the University of Birmingham. viii + 100 pages, with 2 plates. Medium 8vo, 8s. 6d. net.

BIO-CHEMISTRY. A Study of the Origin, Reactions, and Equilibria of Living Matter. By the late BENJAMIN MOORE, M.A., D.Sc., F.R.S. viii + 340 pages. Demy 8vo, 21s. net.

CHEMICAL DISINFECTION AND STERILIZATION. By S. RIDEAL, D.Sc., F.I.C., and E. K. RIDEAL, M.A., D.Sc., F.I.C. 321 pages. Demy 8vo, 21s. net.

SMOKE. A Study of Town Air. By Prof. J. B. COHEN, F.R.S., and Dr. A. G. RUSHTON. SECOND EDITION, with 15 plates. Demy 8vo, 8s. 6d. net.

THE EVOLUTION AND DEVELOPMENT OF THE QUANTUM THEORY. By N. M. BLIGH, A.R.C.S. Demy 8vo, 9s. net.

THE PROBLEM OF PHYSICO-CHEMICAL PERIODICITY. By E. S. HEDGES, Ph.D., and J. E. MYERS, O.B.E., D.Sc. Demy 8vo, 7s. 6d. net.

PHYSICAL CHEMISTRY : its Bearing on Biology and Medicine. By J. C. PHILIP, D.Sc., F.R.S., Professor of Physical Chemistry in the Imperial College of Science and Technology. THIRD EDITION. Crown 8vo, 8s. 6d. net.

ELEMENTARY PHYSICAL CHEMISTRY. By W. H. BARRETT, M.A., Harrow School. viii + 247 pages, with 61 diagrams. 6s.

THE CHEMISTRY OF COLLOIDS AND SOME TECHNICAL APPLICATIONS. By W. W. TAYLOR, M.A., D.Sc., Lecturer in Chemical Physiology in the University of Edinburgh. viii + 332 pages. SECOND EDITION. Crown 8vo, 10s. 6d. net.

PRACTICAL PHOTOMICROGRAPHY. By J. E. BARNARD, F.R.S., and F. V. WELCH, F.R.M.S. SECOND EDITION. xii + 316 pages, with 87 illustrations and 16 plates. Demy 8vo. Cloth, 18s. net.

ANALYTICAL MICROSCOPY. By T. E. WALLIS, B.Sc., Reader in Pharmacognosy in London University. viii + 150 pages. Illustrated. Crown 8vo, cloth, 6s. net.

AN INORGANIC CHEMISTRY. By H. G. DENHAM, M.A., D.Sc., Ph.D., Professor of Chemistry in Canterbury College, University of New Zealand. xii + 684 pages, with 144 diagrams. Crown 8vo, 12s. 6d. net.

INORGANIC CHEMISTRY. A Textbook for Colleges and Schools. By E. J. HOLMYARD, M.A., Head of the Science Department, Clifton College. viii + 564 pages, with 119 diagrams and 10 plates. Crown 8vo, 6s. 6d.

ANALYTICAL PROCESSES : A Physico-Chemical Interpretation. By T. B. SMITH, B.Sc., A.R.C.S., The University, Sheffield. Demy 8vo. 376 pages.

INTERMEDIATE PRACTICAL CHEMISTRY. By E. S. HEDGES, Ph.D., Bedford College, University of London. Demy 8vo. 128 pages.

A HANDBOOK OF ORGANIC ANALYSIS : QUALITATIVE AND QUANTITATIVE. By H. T. CLARKE, B.Sc., A.I.C. xvi + 363 pages. FOURTH EDITION. Crown 8vo, 8s. 6d. net.

AN ELEMENTARY CHEMISTRY. By E. J. HOLMYARD, M.A. viii + 424 pages. Crown 8vo, 5s.

FIRST AID IN THE LABORATORY AND WORKSHOP. By A. A. ELDRIDGE, B.Sc., and H. V. A. BRISCOE, D.Sc. Cloth, 1s. 3d. net.

LONDON : EDWARD ARNOLD & CO., 41 & 43 MADDOX ST., W.1.

BIOLOGY

FOUNDERS OF OCEANOGRAPHY AND THEIR WORK. By Sir WILLIAM HERDMAN, C.B.E., D.Sc., F.R.S. xii + 340 pages, with 29 plates. Demy 8vo, cloth, 21s. net.

MANUAL OF ENTOMOLOGY. By the late H. MAXWELL LEFROY, M.A. xvi + 552 pages. Fully illustrated. Demy 8vo, cloth, 35s. net.

BRITISH HYMENOPTERA. By A. S. BUCKHURST, D.I.C., L. N. STANI-LAND, D.I.C., and G. B. WATSON, D.I.C. Crown 4to, 9s. net.

MAN'S PLACE AMONG THE MAMMALS. By F. WOOD JONES, F.R.S., Professor of Physical Anthropology in the University of Hawaii. Demy 8vo. viii]+ 376 pages, with 158 illustrations and 12 plates. 21s. net.

THE MECHANISM OF LIFE. In Relation to Modern Physical Theory. By J. JOHNSTONE, D.Sc., Professor of Oceanography in the University of Liverpool. xii + 248 pages, with 53 diagrams. Demy 8vo, 15s. net.

A STUDY OF THE OCEANS. By J. JOHNSTONE, D.Sc. Illustrated. Demy 8vo, 10s. 6d. net.

AN INTRODUCTION TO THE SCIENTIFIC STUDY OF THE SOIL. By N. M. COMBER, D.Sc., Professor of Agricultural Chemistry in the University of Leeds. Illustrated. Crown 8vo, 192 pages, 7s. 6d. net.

THE SCIENTIFIC PRINCIPLES OF PLANT PROTECTION. By HUBERT MARTIN, M.Sc. xii + 310 pages. Demy 8vo, 21s. net.

ANIMAL LIFE IN DESERTS. By P. A. BUXTON, M.A. xvi + 172 pages, with 14 plates. Demy 8vo, 10s. 6d. net.

GROWTH. By G. R. DE BEER, B.A., B.Sc., Fellow of Merton College, Oxford. Demy 8vo, 7s. 6d. net.

PRINCIPLES OF BACTERIOLOGY AND IMMUNITY. By W. W. C. TOPLEY, M.A., M.R.C.S., F.R.C.P.; and G. S. WILSON M.D., B.S., of the London School of Hygiene and Tropical Medicine. Super royal. In two volumes.

AN INTRODUCTION TO THE STUDY OF THE PROTOZOA. With special reference to the Parasitic Forms. By the late E. A. MINCHIN, M.A., Ph.D., F.R.S. xii + 520 pages, 194 diagrams. Demy 8vo, 25s. net.

THE MIGRATIONS OF FISH. By ALEXANDER MEEK, M.Sc., F.L.S., F.Z.S. With illustrations and maps. xx + 428 pages. Demy 8vo, 18s. net.

THE DEVELOPMENT OF BRITISH FORESTRY. By A. C. FORBES, F.H.A.S. xii + 274 pages, 70 illustrations. Demy 8vo, 10s. 6d. net.

PROCEEDINGS OF THE WORLD POPULATION CONFERENCE, 1927. Edited by MARGARET SANGER. 383 pages. Medium 8vo. 20s. net.

A HANDBOOK OF THE CONIFERÆ AND GINKGOACEÆ. By W. DALLIMORE and A. B. JACKSON. With 32 plates and 120 diagrams. Medium 8vo, cloth, 42s. net.

A' BRITISH GARDEN FLORA. By Lt.-Col. J. W. C. KIRK, B.A., F.R.H.S., with a foreword by Dr. A. W. HILL, C.M.G., F.R.S. xii + 592 pages, with 223 diagrams. Medium 8vo, 42s. net.

ELEMENTARY BOTANY. An Introduction to the Study of Plant Life. By W. WATSON, D.Sc. viii+368 pages, with 225 diagrams. Crown 8vo, 6s. 6d. net.